Printed and Published in Great Britain by D. C. THOMSON & CO., LTD., 185 Fleet Street, London EC4A 2HS. © D. C. THOMSON & CO., LTD., 1992. **ISBN** 0 85116 538 9

£4.10

Rough guide to

Parties
They're great fun —
or are they?
Read on
to find out
if you've got
party
power!

THE BIRTHDAY PARTY

If you're throwing yourself a birthday party the fact you'll get lots of pressies will make up for people scratching your records, nosing around in your room and breaking the video!

GOOD BITS

The pressies!
You'll feel really popular for an evening.
You can invite whoever you want. Like that hunk from fourth year.
You can demand a birthday kiss from him!
There's a chance someone will actually buy you something that you like!
You don't have to rush to get ready — then you can stroll downstairs!
You can scoff all the food before anyone arrives — and then the leftovers the next day!

BAD BITS

You'll get an awful lot of bath sets 'cos no one "knew what to get you".
The lads'll feel they've got to play a horrible joke on you 'cos it's your birthday.
Your mum will insist you ask your boring and wimpy cousin along.
The creep from next door will want a birthday snog!
You'll have to open your gifts in front of everyone and try to look excited when you get your sixth set of make-up brushes!
Your mum always makes a 'twee' birthday cake.
She'll make you wear the 'smashing blouse' she bought for you.

THE 'MY PARENTS ARE AWAY' PARTY!

You've got to be very brave to throw this party. What might start off as you honestly 'just having a few friends round to watch a video' will soon turn into hundreds of people running wild in your house! Word *always* gets out that your house is 'free' for the evening!

GOOD BITS

If you manage to keep the numbers down it can be quite a good chuckle having your chums over for a gossip.
You can play your records as loudly as you like (well almost!).
Your parents won't be there to embarrass you!
You'll be popular with everyone in your school for an evening.

BAD BITS

Your house will probably get wrecked.
Someone will find the family photo album with your baby pictures in it.
Someone will decide to phone their penpal — in America!

THE FANCY DRESS PARTY

A real hoot! You don't have to wait 'til Hallowe'en either — they're a great laugh whenever you have them!

GOOD BITS

You can spend most of the night laughing at everyone's costume.
Your good clothes will last longer!

BAD BITS

After you've been dancing for half an hour solid you'll realise it might not have been such a good idea to dress up in a gorilla costume as you almost faint!
There's no one to give you a lift to the party, so you've got to get on the bus looking like an idiot.
You'll bump into the guy you've fancied for ages while you're dressed up!

THE OUTSIDE/PARTY BARBECUE

Aaah, no mess in the house with this one!

GOOD BITS

It's a good excuse to stuff your face. Well, it's a shame to let all those barbecued sausages go to waste!
You can look at the stars with the guy of your dreams!
You can join in the footie with the guys!

BAD BITS

It'll rain.
There're never enough seats for everyone.
There'll be insects everywhere — scream!

es

TIDYING UP

No one wants to do it, but if it's your party you'll have to. You'll also have to figure out how to get those crushed crisps and orange juice out of the carpet and know how to glue your mum's favourite ornament together again.

PARTY TOP TIPS

Lock away all the ornaments.
Make up mixture tapes to save your records getting scratched.
Lock your bedroom door otherwise everyone will snoop around your room.
Disconnect the phone!
Be incredibly nice to the neighbours beforehand!
Hide the dog.
Don't have a party!

TOP TIPS

Beg some 'guests' to help you.
Pay some 'guests' to help you!
Spend the entire party running around tidying up after everyone.
Don't have a party!

PARTY PROBLEMS

PARENTS

If you're really unlucky they'll stay 'to keep an eye on things', and your credibility will hit zero. You can't exactly snog the face off the fifth year hunk when your dad's hovering around in the background, can you?

Even if you're lucky enough to get rid of your parents, you can be sure they'll appear home an hour earlier than they said to find your boyfriend dancing on top of their antique table!

HOW TO GET RID OF YOUR PARENTS

Sorry, but you can't!

THE CHRISTMAS PARTY

Yippee! Christmas is the best time for parties — lots of pressies and snogging!

GOOD BITS

Grabbing guys you've fancied all year under the mistletoe!
You'll have your new Christmas togs to wear.
There's always tons of people at them.
Your mum and dad usually let you stay out a little bit later as a Christmas treat!

BAD BITS

Ugly guys will try to snog you under the mistletoe!
They always play naff 'novelty' records at Crimbo parties.
Your new shoes will hurt your feet.

PARTY SPEAK
Learn the lingo!

WHAT YOU'LL HEAR:
"Have you got a cloth?"
WHAT IT MEANS:
"I've just spilled blackcurrant all over your mum's cream-coloured sofa."

WHAT YOU'LL HEAR:
"Well it was working a minute ago."
WHAT IT MEANS:
"I've just broken your big brother's v. expensive hi-fi."

WHAT YOU'LL HEAR:
"I just went somewhere for a bit of peace and quiet"
WHAT IT MEANS:
"I've been in your room looking for your diary."

WHAT YOU'LL HEAR:
"I'm starving!"
WHAT IT MEANS:
"Can we raid your fridge?"

WHAT YOU'LL HEAR:
"Can I bring a friend to your party?"
WHAT IT MEANS:
"Can I bring 10 friends to your party?"

WHAT YOU'LL HEAR:
"Why don't you change the music?"
WHAT IT MEANS:
"This party's really boring."

A — ATTITUDE

Well, we're sorry to say that a lot of the time it stinks. Lads often feel that they've got a birrovan appearance to keep up in front of other lads. Y'know the sort of thing we mean — he acts all sort of cool, blasé and attempts to 'wise crack'. It can be quite annoying at times but if you think he's worth the effort, given time, he'll improve and you should end up with a pussycat.

B — BAD BOYS

We girls can't seem to help it . . . one glimpse of a mean lookin' guy with a floppy fringe and a scowl and we find ourselves hooked! Are we looking for Mr Wrong . . . or what? If you've got the willpower, avoid him at all costs — he'll be so busy being a tortured soul, dates 'n' romance'll go straight out of the window. If no willpower exists, join the ranks of many a broken-hearted 'cos he'll never change!

C — CUDDLING

Never, ever attempt a hug when his mates are around — 'cos you're bound to be disappointed. Lads do love a cuddle just as much as we do but not when there are witnesses. He's got to keep up the image!

D — DATING

When it comes to the dating game and they eventually get around to asking you out, they'll need a bit of guidance on what to do 'cos otherwise you'll just end up going to look at the goal posts where he made his first 'save'! A few 'cheap' suggestions should be most welcome if he's a bit low on imagination.

E — EMOTIONS

Sorry to say lads are a bit reserved about letting the more tender emotions show. Most of them would like to pretend that they're purritty cool and nothing hassles them, but if you become good enough at recognising the tell tale signs you'll know that's not exactly true! When it comes down to it, just letting him know you'll be there if he needs you will be much appreciated.

F — FRIENDS

Even though you find his friends to be a complete pain in the neck . . . he'll most definitely resent it if you try to come between them. If you don't actually like any of his friends in particular your best bet is just to avoid being in their company. Don't 'bad mouth' them to him. How would you feel if he slagged off your mates?

G — GOOSEBUMPS

While maintaining the 'cool' act most lads are also too darn good at hiding the fact that a kiss or six and some affection has exactly the same effect on him as it has on us . . . a few shivers and some goosebumps.

H — HOLDING HANDS

Tricky one this. Depending on the lad in question, mitt-gripping could either be a complete no-no to be avoided at all costs or something he'll just do naturally. If you're unsure, you could try testing the water when you're alone together. He'll soon let you know what he prefers.

I — INSECURE

Of course they are. Think about it — exactly how paranoid and 'iffy' would you feel if you didn't get the chance to air all your thoughts and worries during a heart to heart with the girls? Well, lads don't 'share' things like us girlies do, so they never get any reassurance. They're bound to feel a little insecure at times!

J — JEALOUSY

All of us suffer from the ol' green-eyed monster from time to time but if he's jealous of you and some other lad, all he'll need is a bit of reassurance that it's him you want to be with. But, if he's coming down really hard on you 'cos you don't spend every minute of the day with him, forget him — these dark possessive types aren't worth the hassle. Honest!

K — KISSING

Under a certain age they think it's 'soft' then all of a sudden they think it's fabsy. Grab them at the latter stage for some nifty practice.

L — LOVE

Well, they love football, their mums and lasagne . . . but girlies? Girls are just for having a laugh with and snogging. Don't you believe it — every lad wants to love and be loved . . . getting them to admit it is the hard bit!!

getting on with yer lad will be a whole lot easier . . . once you've read our A-Z.

THE A-Z of BOYS

M — MUM

Yip, his mother. Remember he's always (no matter what he's done) going to be her little ray of sunshine, so make sure you get her as an ally. She'll always be good for a few embarrassing photos 'n' stories on a cold evening.

N — NICKNAMES

Lads have a strange fascination for finding little 'pet' names for one another — like Deebo, Gruff, Tonka or such like. The history of such a name usually involves some boring story of a school football trip — best avoided altogether. But, as a warning, if you find a little pet name for him — he won't relish you calling him it with other people around!

OBSTACLES —

Trying to chat to any lad about your relationship is, to be honest, like drawing teeth — most lads'll do anything to avoid a confrontation — if they know it's coming. Best thing is to surprise him with the subject — this way you'll get his honest reaction.

PARENTS —

To him, meeting your parents is akin to facing a court martial, so don't be too surprised if he tries to worm his way out of every little get-together you set up. The way to get him in the door is to stress how completely informal the whole thing is and how yer dad supports the same footie team — even if you're sure your mum's got the lights and thumb-screws set up!

QUESTIONS —

Now, the thing about asking questions like 'What are you thinking?' or such like, is that either it'll be so boring you'll wish you'd never asked . . . or it can be interpreted as nagging . . . y'see there's a fine line between natural curiosity and 'nagging' as far as lads are concerned!

RIDICULE —

As we've already more than hinted at, most lads live in mortal fear of what their mates are going to say about anything and everything. The most important thing about being a lad in a group is fitting in — and being the object of 'fun' over a girlie is not desirable! That's why he tends to look shifty and shuffles off if you approach when he's . . . ahem, busy!

SWEARING —

Now, given the fact that they are out to impress and that they spend nearly all their time with other lads, a boy can be known to drop a few 'humdingers' into an otherwise pleasant conversation. Ignoring it the first time is OK — but if he does it again, launching into the 'It's not big and it's not clever' lecture — won't do any harm. Just let him know it's not impressing you!

TEMPERS —

Most lads, when in the midst of a tantrum, become surprisingly hard of hearing when it comes to reason — that is, they only hear what they want to. Give him plenty of time to cool off . . . i.e. just about enough for him to be feeling stupid and stop sulking and then tactfully and gently broach the subject again. Well, have you never lost your temper?

UNDERSTANDING —

You say . . . "So, where are you off to tonight?" He hears, "Where are you going and who with? Anyone I know? Is it a girl? When will you get back?" etc. It's a fact, we don't always speak exactly the same language and mix-ups often occur. Explaining thoughts, feelings and reasoning now and again always helps.

VANITY —

Although he may not look as though he's spent a lot of time on his appearance, we can assure you he's spent loads of time getting his fringe to flop just so. Yip, boys worry about spots etc. as well. A bit of reassurance about his looks goes down well, but not too much — lads have been known to get carried away.

WEAKNESSES —

Most folks have them — whether it be chocolate or otherwise — but lads often see them as a failing point so be a love and when you find out what they are — don't use them to your advantage . . . too often!

X-RATED —

His bedroom. Don't go in unless you're wearing protective clothing and never ever look under the bed 'cos even his adoring mum won't. 'Nuff said!

YAWN —

Next time he's launching into a particularly yawn-inspiring story about football or the like, just remember how you dragged the poor lad round every make-up counter in the land looking for 'pink sunrise with extra cherry' lippy . . . Would that have been fun for him? Unlikely!!!

ZITS —

Yes they get them. Yes, they hate them . . . And no, they won't really notice yours!!

SPRING

Spring into action with the season's fruitiest colours.

Spring Fling!

SPRING SHADES

Go for the brightest shades of yellow, green, orange and turquoise — indeed anything with a fresh and fruity feel to it.

 Top and skirt by Naughty. Baseball boots from Dolcis.

MAKE-UP

Go for the freshest look using minimal make-up.

THE BASE — After the winter you're more than likely to be quite pasty and suffering from dry skin, so go for a moisturising liquid foundation. Apply using a latex sponge for a light coverage. Use just a puff of the finest translucent powder to keep your foundation intact, but not enough to make it look as though it's matt.

EYES — A light smudge of a milk chocolate brown colour over your lower lids and blended to nothing at either side of your eyes and socket will give you subtle definition. Use a brown — or brown black if you've dark colouring — mascara which will 'open' your eyes without making them look over made-up. Remember to brush your eyebrows into place, darkening them with a *little* of the eyeshadow to even out their shape.

LIPS — We used a moisturising tea-rose lipstick but any transparent colour works a treat. Applied with a brush it lasts longer and gives a better finish.

SPRING THING!

● Get into a Spring-like mood by wearing loads of different colours. Now's *not* the time to be moodsome in black!

● If you're a little pale there's no harm in just a *touch* of blusher. Use the largest fluffiest brush you can find and puff it onto the round of your cheeks. A hint of colour is sufficient!

● If Spring goes to your head and you feel you've gotta have a change of style, be sure to chat with your stylist before letting them run riot with your crowning glory. Take along a few piccies of the sorta style you'd like and remember that it's you who's paying . . . and you're the one who's got to wear it!

● It's still a bit 'fresh' in Spring so go for bright opaque tights. There's nowt more unattractive than chilly thighs sticking out from a mini.

● Remember summer follows Spring, so start preparing for the beach now! Cut down on the 'bad' foods (crisps, choccy, burgers, etc.) and incorporate a few healthier foodstuffs (yum scrum yoghurt, mucho fruit, veg and wholemeal things) and do a bit of exercise every other day! This'll stop depression hitting you come shorts and halterneck time!

● The essential Spring beauty buy is a lighter coverage foundation — bare all!

● The essential Spring fashion buy is a beezer blazer! Wear it with jeans, leggings, mini skirts, a big shirt . . . the possibilities are endless!

SM

Everyone warms to a lovely smile, so make sure yours is in tip top condition . . .

TEETH TIPS

Firstly, there's no point in giving wide cheesers and revealing a set of grotty teeth! Take good care of 'em, 'cos if you don't, you'll regret it for the rest of your life.

The first step in the right direction is to cut down on foods which are high in sugar, that means goodies like sweets and fizzy drinks (BIG teeth enemies!!). Removing plaque is next in the line of defence. Plaque is a thin, sticky film of bacteria (yuk!) which clings to your teeth. Not only is it bad for teeth, but for your gums too as it can cause inflammation and lead to gum disease. Warning signs are red, swollen gums which bleed when you brush your teeth. If that sounds familiar then a visit to your dentist is in order!

FLOSSING FUN!

Flossing is essential for good tooth care and you should always floss before brushing. Take about 25cm of dental floss and pass it between two teeth. Work it gently into the gum crevice then down to the biting surface, pulling against the adjoining tooth. It can be quite difficult to manage correctly, so why not ask your dentist to show you how it's done and advise you how often your teeth need flossed?

FIT FOR NOTHING?!

Jogging and swimming or slobbing around — what's for you?

ILE!

BRUSHING

You should brush your teeth at least twice a day, in the morning, at night and preferably after meals too. It's a good idea to carry a Body Shop Denty-Box around with you to use during the day.

Hold your brush at a 45 degree angle to the gum, so that it can work into the gum pockets around the teeth. Brush with a gentle scrubbing motion, concentrating on one or two teeth at a time. Remember to do the back of your teeth too!

To leave your mouth feeling clean, slush round some cold water and spit it out . . . don't swallow!

Use disclosing tablets regularly to check you're not missing bits out.

We've all been caught showing off our pearlies, only to be told we've got a bit of broccoli stuck in 'em! Be prepared, when you're out for a romantic dinner, carry a small mirror, hold it where he can't see and check for those naughty bits of broccoli!

LIP CARE

Your lips must be kept well moisturised as they have no sebaceous glands, so it's up to you to take good care of them. Dry, cracked lips are decidedly unattractive, not to mention unkissable! Wind and cold weather can cause cracked lips which are more likely to become infected and develop cold sores or blisters. You can buy ointments to help cure them, but if the sores persist it's worth a visit to your doctor to get 'em sorted out.

LIP TIPS

● Always wear a lip balm when you're out in the cold. (The Body Shop's Morello Cherry one is pretty scrummy!)

● When using a facial scrub always avoid your lips. Try using your toothbrush, after you've brushed your teeth, in small circular movements to gently slough away any rough bits.

● Irritations can be caused by the dyes in lipsticks, so if you're sensitive try out a hypo-allergenic, unperfumed brand that doesn't contain indelible dyes.

LIPSTICK TRICKS

Let's face it, for a perfect pout, you've got to have perfect lipstick. Nothing looks worse than smudged or uneven lipstick and you'd probably look better without it! Take a few tips from us . . .

● When you're applying your foundation, make sure you smooth a little over your lips (not too much, though, or it'll just go into clumps . . . blurgh!). Then apply a little powder for a perfectly dry base for your lipstick. This blots any moisture and helps the colour last.

● Outline your lips very carefully with either a lip pencil or a lipbrush coated in a shade that tones with your chosen lip colour. This stops the colour from 'bleeding'. Don't worry if you don't get it right at first, practice makes perfect!

● Soften the line by dabbing gently with a cotton bud, or even a clean fingertip.

● Now apply your lipstick, within the line and always with a lipbrush.

● Blot your mouth with a tissue and a light dusting of powder.

● Reapply the colour, and give your lips a quick dusting of translucent powder to give a matt look.

● And don't lick your lips! Even the longest-lasting lip colour won't stand up to this!

SMILE FILE

Now that you know the basics, put that cheeser to good use! Any girl knows that a winning smile can get you what you want, such as . . .

1. The bloke you're after. Give the sultry, mysterious look a miss and treat him to your best, most natural smile ever. How could he refuse?

2. When you've not done your homework! Oops . . . if you've got that 'innocent' look about you, use it to its full advantage! A wide 'sorry' type smile works wonders in these situations, instead of a huffy 'I can't be bothered' look!

3. Horror of horrors! You've been caught bitching and she heard every word! What a nightmare . . . don't draw her a dagger with your eyes, give her a wide smile, apologise and hopefully her anger will fade . . .

4. When your dad's being a pain and insisting on picking you up at the disco at 9.30 p.m. opt for the sunny 'golden daughter' face, not the 'spoilt brat' one! Hopefully he'll give in to you, just this once . . .

Exercise is a purritty good idea when . . .

● you're bored and you've played every single game of Monop., Triv. and Cluedo in the house.

● someone affectionately calls you 'Hippo' . . . nmphh!

● your weight doesn't register on the scales.

● when *he* exercises at the gym!

● loose fit jeans are skin tight on you.

● you collapse in a pathetic heap at the top of one measly flight of stairs.

● your P.E. teacher uses you as an example of how a fit, healthy teenager should *not* look.

● you get out of your seat in the café so you can swan past him, only to watch all the glasses on the table topple over, 'cos your bottom's bumped off it in a big way.

● you've seen a very unflattering party photo of yourself with three sweating chins . . .

● you get stuck against people, shuffling to your seat in the cinema . . .

It's not a good idea when . . .

▶ you're depressed.

▶ your tennis/jogging/swimming partner is the school superchamp!

▶ you've just stuffed your face with an entire box of Mr Kipling's Country Slices.

▶ 'Brookside' is on.

▶ . . . or when he's going to call you!

▶ it's colder than 10 degrees outside, drizzling rain, snowing, hailstones, cloudy . . .

▶ chocolates, not jogging, is the only way to cheer yerself up when you've had a fight with your best chum!

▶ you look silly/gross/fatter in baggy clothes, pastel shades, swimsuits and anything else remotely sporty.

▶ you're slagged rotten, whistled and sniggered at by your entire family every time you set foot outside the house, complete with towelling headband and sports bag.

▶ you don't feel like it!

TOP TWINS

Double the fun with this lot!

BROS — ▲
Cor! Two hunks in the one family! The Goss boys sing as good as they look!

GAIL AND GILLIAN BLAKENY —
Real-life twins who played soap twins — the Allessis in 'Neighbours'. Gail snogs Stefan Dennis in real life too!

PAULINE FOWLER AND PETE BEALE —
Erm, 'Easties' most 'glamorous' twins don't even look like each other — thankfully!

LLOYD AND HATTIE TAVERNIER —
More 'Easties' twins!

STEVE AND ANDY McDONALD — ▲
'Coronation Street's' blond 'n' gorgeous twins give us two good reasons to tune in!

CAROL AND MARK THATCHER —
Yup, their mummy is ex-Prime Minister, Margaret!

TWIN

TWINS ON SCREEN

Double trouble movies!

'DOUBLE IMPACT' —
A double dose of gorgeous Jean Claude van Damme 'cos he plays a pair of tough-talkin' brothers.

'DEAD RINGERS' —
Gangly Jeremy Irons plays a spooky pair of twins in this horror flick.

'BIG BUSINESS' —
Lilly Tomlin AND Bette Midler both play sets of twins in this comedy!

'A KISS BEFORE DYING' —
Sean Young is a pair of sisters who both fall for the fatal charm of Matt Dillon. Unfortunately there's only one of him!

'BULLSEYE' —
Golden oldies Roger Moore and Michael Caine play doublers in this romp. Isn't one of each enough?!

'THE KRAYS' —
Evil twins Ronnie and Reggie are played by hunky brothers Martin and Gary Kemp!

peeks....

'TWINS' — ▶
Danny Devito and big Arnie Schwarzenegger play, er, twins!

'TWINS OF EVIL' —
A not-too-scary horror flick about vampire twin sisters!

'A STOLEN LIFE' —
Bette Davis plays twins — a nice one and a rather nasty one who steals her sister's boyfriend!

SPOOKY TWIN FACTS!

There are a record number of 36 sets of twins on the remote island of North Uist in the Outer Hebrides!

The longest interval between the birth of twins occurred when one was born on December 23, 1987 and the other one didn't come along 'til January 30, 1988!

The oldest recorded twins ever lived until they were 108. They both died in the same year!

TWIN TALES

The saucy twin dancers from Prince's 'Cream' video of last year impressed him so much he decided to date them both!

Elvis Presley had a twin brother who sadly died shortly after he was born.

Linda Hamilton of 'Terminator' and 'Terminator 2' fame used to get her twin sister to pretend she was Linda — it worked out fine until Arnie Schwarzenegger pinched her bum and got a quick 'cuff round the ear'!

Matt and Luke Goss claim to be able to speak to each other telepathically — as do a lot o' twins!

WHAT A RESULT!

LISA

'We never wear make-up, we always wear jeans and we reckon we need a change!' wrote Lisa on behalf of her five-a-side football team. It was an offer we couldn't refuse . . . the Jackie make-over team tackled it and scored a winner over the lot of 'em . . .

Well, girls, what did you think of your new look?

Different! Totally different! I loved the dress . . . but it tickled a bit! It's not like anything I've ever worn in my whole life, my boyfriend won't know me! I'd maybe wear it for a special occasion. I thought the make-up was pretty outrageous! I never wear make-up, so it was quite a surprise when I saw myself.

MARGUARIT

COLETTE

I never, ever, ever wear skirts so it was a real shock seeing myself in that dress! It's gorgeous but it felt like I was wearing a corset . . . what a change from jeans and a T-shirt! I've never worn anything like that before! I liked the make-up, although I thought the eyeshadow was quite heavy. I really love the shade of lipstick, in fact I think I'll buy it! But, overall, what a shocker it was seeing myself dressed up!

Well, I must admit I'm a bit of a tomboy and I never wear skirts or dresses. The dress I wore was great and I loved the colour. I might just be persuaded to wear something like that now. I liked the make-up too, but what a surprise it was! I never thought I could look so, well, sort of . . . 'girlie'!

SUSAN

LAURA

I always wear really casual stuff, but I might be tempted to wear something different now. The hairdo is totally different and I thought the make-up was quite heavy, but that's just because I'm not used to it! I loved the colours the make-up artist used, and again, like everyone else I'm amazed at the difference in me.

I'd wear the hotpants, but not the top I'm afraid! It's just not something I feel comfy in! The hairdo was totally different, so was the make-up! Yeah, it's a shock to see myself like that! Wow!

MARGUARIT
Green velvet dress from River Island.

LISA
Black velvet feathered dress from Top Shop.

COLETTE
Red dress from River Island.

LAURA
Red velvet top from Top Shop and black velvet hotpants from Miss Selfridge.

SUSAN
Grey jacket and black leggings from River Island.

hots: Martin at Upfront.   Hair and make-up: Suzanne Hurles.

WORK IT

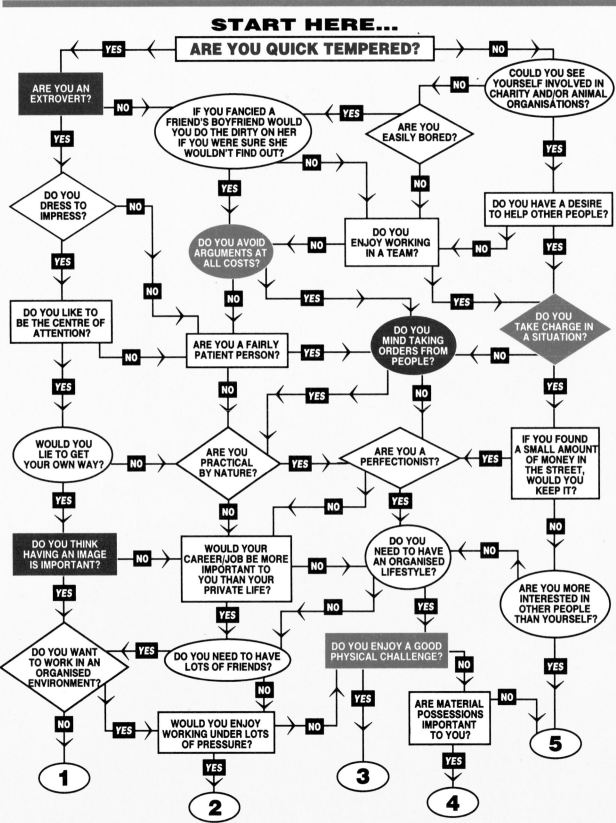

START HERE...

ARE YOU QUICK TEMPERED?

ARE YOU AN EXTROVERT?

COULD YOU SEE YOURSELF INVOLVED IN CHARITY AND/OR ANIMAL ORGANISATIONS?

IF YOU FANCIED A FRIEND'S BOYFRIEND WOULD YOU DO THE DIRTY ON HER IF YOU WERE SURE SHE WOULDN'T FIND OUT?

ARE YOU EASILY BORED?

DO YOU DRESS TO IMPRESS?

DO YOU HAVE A DESIRE TO HELP OTHER PEOPLE?

DO YOU AVOID ARGUMENTS AT ALL COSTS?

DO YOU ENJOY WORKING IN A TEAM?

DO YOU LIKE TO BE THE CENTRE OF ATTENTION?

ARE YOU A FAIRLY PATIENT PERSON?

DO YOU MIND TAKING ORDERS FROM PEOPLE?

DO YOU TAKE CHARGE IN A SITUATION?

WOULD YOU LIE TO GET YOUR OWN WAY?

ARE YOU PRACTICAL BY NATURE?

ARE YOU A PERFECTIONIST?

IF YOU FOUND A SMALL AMOUNT OF MONEY IN THE STREET, WOULD YOU KEEP IT?

DO YOU THINK HAVING AN IMAGE IS IMPORTANT?

WOULD YOUR CAREER/JOB BE MORE IMPORTANT TO YOU THAN YOUR PRIVATE LIFE?

DO YOU NEED TO HAVE AN ORGANISED LIFESTYLE?

ARE YOU MORE INTERESTED IN OTHER PEOPLE THAN YOURSELF?

DO YOU WANT TO WORK IN AN ORGANISED ENVIRONMENT?

DO YOU NEED TO HAVE LOTS OF FRIENDS?

DO YOU ENJOY A GOOD PHYSICAL CHALLENGE?

ARE MATERIAL POSSESSIONS IMPORTANT TO YOU?

WOULD YOU ENJOY WORKING UNDER LOTS OF PRESSURE?

1 2 3 4 5

OUT!

1 · *ARTS*

Singing, acting, dancing, modelling, creative writing, painting.

You're the extrovert type who likes to show off in a big way! You like attention, love the idea of fame and would probably be v. happy indeed working in a relaxed and easy-going atmosphere, when the amount of work is up to you! You dislike being told what to do, and hate the idea of restrictions in any sort of job! A true star!

2 · *MEDIA*

TV, journalism, advertising, PR, fashion, researching.

Dynamic, tough and argumentative on occasion, that's you! You thrive on new challenges, pushing things until you get what you want. You relate well to other people and like to work using your own initiative, without being bossed around! These jobs would be ideal for you as they also give you the chance to use your imagination - perfect for the pushy type!

3 · *PHYSICAL/SKILLED*

Mechanical, the armed forces, police, farming, firefighter.

You like to get out 'n' about on your job - not stuck indoors all day, and work well in a team situation! You like to be given opportunities to prove yourself and are a logical, sensible type of gal, enjoying physical activity in your work. You're also disciplined, making you ideal for the tough kinda jobs most girls keep well away from!

4 · *CLERICAL*

Secretarial, banking, accountancy, travel agent, civil service, solicitor.

If you landed with this, the chances are you're the organised type! You like a neat orderly lifestyle, and plod your way through things slowly and methodically, leaving no stone unturned! You're level-headed, capable and ain't afraid of responsibility - no siree!

5 · *CARING*

Nursing, teaching, social worker, charity, veterinary nurse.

You're a caring, sensitive type of girl who's honest and darned trustworthy into the bargain! You're also resourceful, capable and no problem's too big for you to cope with! You dislike competitiveness, preferring to work at your own pace with no outside pressure, and hate authority, making people listen to what you've got to say - and it's no bad thing!

THREE LITTLE WORDS

RYAN WAS CRAZY ABOUT HIS GIRLFRIEND, LAURA . . .

WE'VE BEEN TOGETHER FOR NEARLY FIVE MONTHS NOW, LAURA, AND IT'S BEEN BRILLIANT . . . I JUST WANT TO TELL YOU — THAT I LOVE YOU . . .

WELL, I'M NOT SAYING THAT — IT SOUNDS WELL CORNY! HOW DO YOU TELL YOUR GIRLFRIEND YOU LOVE HER WITHOUT SOUNDING LIKE A PRAT?

I KNOW I SHOULD BE TELLING LAURA HOW I FEEL ABOUT HER AFTER BEING TOGETHER FOR FIVE MONTHS BUT SOMEHOW I JUST CAN'T GET UP THE NERVE TO DO IT. ANYWAY, WHAT IF SHE DIDN'T SAY IT BACK TO ME? I'D DIE OF EMBARRASSMENT!

STILL, IF I KEEP PRACTISING, MAYBE ONE DAY I'LL GET ROUND TO DOING IT!

LAURA, I'VE GOT SOMETHING TO TELL YOU . . .

I LOVE YOU — YOU'RE WONDERFUL!

YUK!

OI, YOU BRAT, DIDN'T ANYONE TEACH YOU TO KNOCK ON A DOOR BEFORE YOU COME IN?

YEAH, BUT I THOUGHT IT'D BE A NICE SURPRISE FOR YOU IF I JUST CAME RIGHT IN INSTEAD! WHAT'RE YOU DOING?

NONE OF YOUR BUSINESS!

I KNOW ANYWAY. I WAS LISTENING OUTSIDE THE DOOR! 'OH, LAURA, LAURA, I LOVE YOU!'

YOU LITTLE CREEP!

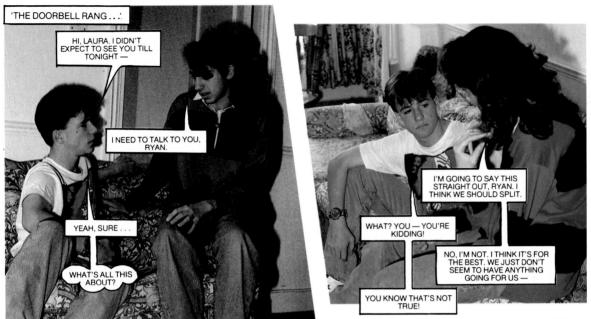

THE END

You don't need to buy up every beauty product you see — just invest in a few essentials!

beauty

CLEAN UP

For glowing skin, you should have a daily cleansing routine and the right products!
You'll need:

CLEANSER:

There are heaps to choose from so look around to get one that suits your skin type. Spotty skins should avoid anything too astringent which could cause irritation — go for one that's simple and fragrance-free. Dry skin'll need a creamier formula that won't strip away natural oils.

FACIAL WASH:

If you like washing your face, use a facial wash instead of soap. Choose a soap-free formula and lather it over your face and don't forget to rinse well.

EXFOLIATOR:

A facial scrub is a must to prevent dull, greasy skin. A good scrub a couple of times a week'll remove dead skin cells and boost circulation. Choose from gels and creams with fine particles, or use a facial brush/pad with your regular face wash.

FACE MASK:

Use one of these once a week to deep cleanse and tighten your pores. Make sure you use the right type for your skin or you could end up doing more harm than good!

MOISTURISER:

Every skin needs moisturiser. It helps to seal in the natural oil and water, keeping your skin soft and silky!

MAKIN'-UP

You don't need hundreds of cosmetics — a few well chosen items should do the trick.
You'll need:

FOUNDATION:

Pick one that suits your skin colour and skin type. There's no use going for a moisturising brown panstick if you've got fair, greasy skin! The better your skin, the less you'll need, so why not try a tinted moisturiser if you're blemish-free?

CONCEALER:

These usually come in swivel sticks or creams. Choose one that matches your foundation and apply it with a fine brush or a cotton bud to blend it with your foundation.

POWDER:

A pat of loose, translucent powder should suit everyone. Apply it with a velvet-soft powder puff or a big, fluffy brush.

BLUSHER:

Choose from powder or cream blushers, although powder ones are better for young skins 'cos they aren't so heavy. Apply after powder to the plumpest bit of your cheeks!

EYESHADOW:

Two or three toning shades should do the trick! You'll need a pale highlighting shade and a couple of darker shadows to add depth and colour. Go for matt ones if possible.

basics

MASCARA:

This gives even the palest lashes a lick of colour and defines your eyes. If you've got pale hair and skin use a brown mascara 'cos black can look too harsh.

LIPSTICK:

The right lipstick can really set your make-up off so go for a couple of neutral, daytime colours plus a luscious red or pinky/plum for night-time. Use a lipbrush to outline your lips first then fill in the rest.

HAIR CARE

Healthy hair needs a bit of tender, loving care, but that doesn't mean splurging out on heaps of unnecessary products! You'll need:

SHAMPOO:

Always use a proper shampoo if possible. 'Shampoo and conditioner in one bottle' varieties are OK once in a while, but for regular use, choose one to suit your hair — dry, permed hair has different needs than greasy hair.

CONDITIONER:

Use conditioner after every shampoo to keep your hair soft 'n' shiny and to help protect against split, dry ends.

For extra help, use an intensive conditioner once a week, especially on longer locks that can be quite dry at the ends.

STYLING:

There are loads to pick from so shop around and go for whatever suits your hairstyle. Choose from mousse, gel, wax and sprays.

ON THE NAIL

Healthy nails look great but they take a bit of effort to get them that way! A regular manicure, say, once a week should give you good results. **You'll need:**

VARNISH REMOVER:

A non-oily remover is a must to keep nails clean and wipe away chipped polish.

EMERY BOARD:

Use the fine side of an emery board to file nails into a neat, rounded shape.

ORANGE STICK:

Wrap a piece of cotton wool round the end and gently push back the cuticles (at the base of your nail).

HANDCREAM:

Keep your hands soft and nails moisturised to prevent splitting with a good hand and nail cream. Use it after you've washed your hands or whenever they've been in water. Great for protecting them in cold weather, too!

NAIL POLISH:

A clear or pale pink/peach varnish applied after your manicure will give nails a well cared for, polished look.

EXTRA ESSENTIALS!

Those little items that make all the difference!

● Brushes — a good set of long handled make-up brushes will give your make-up a professional finish.

● Cotton wool — you don't need expensive stuff so check out the baby care section of your local chemist for a cheaper variety.

● Cotton buds — great for applying make-up, blending and correcting mistakes.

BODY

All the things a girl has to go through can seem a bit daunting . . . so, especially for you, we've compiled the great growing-up guide . . .

SHAPING UP

Yip, although we girlies come in all shapes 'n' sizes, very few of us are actually completely happy with our lot . . . and when the dreaded 'puberty' arrives it has been known to give us a birrova turn. Knowing what to expect and that practically the same things happen to every girlie can certainly avoid any unnecessary worry.

● One of the first things you'll notice is that your trusty vest may have to bow out in favour of a bra for your budding breasts. It is important to choose firm, comfortable support when your bust is developing — but don't worry 'cos there are plenty of pretty styles of bra around especially designed for a developing bust . . . you're sure to find one you like. When your breasts are growing you might find that they get tender and sore — don't worry about it — but this is exactly when a good bra will help.

● Most of you will also notice that your hips will start to look a bit 'rounder' and shapelier and your waist will become thinner. This again is just your body shaping up into its mature form.

● You'll find that body hair makes an appearance in places it's never been before . . . like under your arms and between your legs. You might find that your legs get hairier as well.

These changes are all completely natural and can happen at varying stages, so don't worry if you aren't 'maturing' at the same rate as your chums. It all evens out in the end!

THAT TIME AGAIN

As well as all the noticeable physical changes you'll see, your body will also be moving to a new stage 'inside'.

Roughly between the ages of about 10 and 16 (don't worry if it's a little earlier or later, everyone is different) — you'll start your menstrual cycle — your periods.

Every month, the average being about 28 days, your body forms a lining in your womb to cushion and protect the egg that

MATTERS

travels down from your ovaries . . . if the egg is fertilised then it will imbed in the lining but if not, both the lining and the egg are discarded by your body to make way for the beginning of the next cycle and the next egg. So, the blood that passes out of your body during your period is just the lining!

Your period can last between three and eight days and you'll use either towels (pads worn externally) or tampons (worn internally — there are instructions in the packets) to catch the flow of blood. Remember, to stay fresh, you should change your towel or tampon regularly.

Although the period flow itself doesn't hurt at all — there are a few other 'discomforts' you may suffer from during your cycle.

● A slightly bloated and hard, sore feeling around your tummy and breasts can mean you are suffering from water retention. This is very common and most girls find eating light meals with plenty of fibre, gentle exercise and cutting down on their intake of caffeine and salt helps.

● Another very common complaint is an irritated and generally moody feeling. This is known as Pre Menstrual Syndrome (PMS). Plenty of sleep and learning a few relaxation methods helps, but if you find that you are really suffering, why not go and see your doctor? There are plenty of things he or she could suggest you try — it's just a matter of finding what works best for you!

● Painful periods are usually caused by muscle contractions in the womb. Taking mild pain-killers will help. It sounds a bit silly but if you can, taking the pain-killer before your tummy actually gets too sore will save a lot of discomfort. A hot-water bottle on your stomach is another good idea as heat will help relax the contracting muscles. If the pain gets bad enough to stop you going out etc. quite regularly, a quick visit to the doc's will help.

STAY FRESH

With all the rest of the things happening to your body, you may also notice that you'll sweat a bit more, this is because you're developing adult sweat glands. So, read on if you feel the need for a stay fresh guide.

1) A shower or bath in the morning is a fabsy way to waken up and freshen up! Choose a fruity soap or shower gel, give yourself a good buffing over with loads of lather and you'll feel great. Remember to tie your hair back off your face if you're not going to wash it.

2) Now cleanse your face, using a mild cleanser and some gentle circular movements with cotton wool. Now tone and moisturise and your skin'll stay clean, shiny and hopefully blemish-free.

3) After patting yourself dry with a towel, applying some light body lotion will stop your skin from drying out.

4) Use an anti-perspirant deodorant under your arms to keep yourself fresh all day. They come in spray, solid or roll-on form and are just the biz to keep you smelling sweet.

5) Opt for clean undies and tights every day and try to stick to wearing 'natural' fabrics such as cotton or wool as, unlike synthetic fabrics, they 'breathe' and allow you to keep cool and comfortable.

BODY TIPS

● Occasionally, especially around the time of your period, you could find you break out in a crop of spots. What to do is simply keep your skin clean and oil-free using gentle products then apply a mild antiseptic to any blemishes you have. After that, leave well alone, as picking at them will only spread the infection.

● You might notice that your hair gets a little greasier before your period, wash gently with a mild shampoo, but don't scrub too hard, you could end up over stimulating natural oils and making things worse.

● If you feel awkward about how your body's changing, just try to remember that every girl goes through this 'change' and things will eventually settle down. Keep your diet well-balanced with plenty of fresh fruit, veg, fibre and remember to exercise a little and you should feel fabsy!

STAR FILES

KEANU REEVES

Born: 1964 in Beirut.

What you've seen him in:
'ACT OF VENGEANCE' (1984)
'UNDER THE INFLUENCE' (1986)
'YOUNGBLOOD' (1986)
'BROTHERHOOD OF JUSTICE' (1986)
'BABES IN TOYLAND' (1986)
'I WISH I WERE 18 AGAIN' (1987)
'RIVER'S EDGE' (1987)
'BILL AND TED'S EXCELLENT ADVENTURE' (1988)
'PERMANENT RECORD' (1988)
'THE PRINCE OF PENNSYLVANIA' (1988)
'DANGEROUS LIAISONS' (1988)
'THE NIGHT BEFORE' (1988)
'PARENTHOOD' (1989)
'I LOVE YOU TO DEATH' (1990)
'AUNT JULIA AND THE SCRIPTWRITER' (1990)
'POINT BREAK' (1991)
'BILL AND TED'S BOGUS JOURNEY' (1991)
'MY OWN PRIVATE IDAHO' (1992)
Hobbies: Riding his motorbikes — and falling off them! He also goes camping (?) and likes to hang out with his buddies.
Friends: Keanu's good mates with River Phoenix. They've appeared in two movies together — 'I Love You To Death' and 'My Own Private Idaho'. He's also been known to hang out with Patrick Swayze who taught him how to skydive in 'Point Break'!
Lurve: At the moment lovely Keanu's single!

WINONA RYDER

Born: 1971 in the USA.

What you've seen her in:
'LUCAS' (1986)
'SQUAREDANCE' (1987)
'BEETLEJUICE' (1988)
'1969' (1988)
'HEATHERS' (1989)
'GREAT BALLS OF FIRE' (1990)
'MERMAIDS' (1990)
'EDWARD SCISSORHANDS' (1991)
'L.A.NEWYORKPARISROMEHELSINKI' (1991)
'IT'S YOUR FUNERAL' (1992)
'BRAM STOKER'S DRACULA' (1992)
Hobbies: When Winona isn't making movies (which she is ALL the time!), she hangs out in her apartment in New York, buys antique books and snogs Johnny Depp!
Friends: If Winona had a party the guest list would be rather impressive! Her buddies include Cher, Jodie Foster, Michael Keaton, Christian Slater and Kiefer Sutherland!
Lurve: Johnny Depp is Winona's true love and by the time you read this they'll probably be married!

CHRISTIAN SLATER

Born: 1968 in the USA.

What you've seen him in:
'THE LEGEND OF BILLIE JEAN' (1985)
'THE NAME OF THE ROSE' (1986)
'TUCKER' (1988)
'GLEAMING THE CUBE' (1988)
'BEYOND THE STARS' (1989)
'HEATHERS' (1989)
'TALES FROM THE DARKSIDE' (1990)
'THE WIZARD' (1990)
'YOUNG GUNS II' (1990)
'PUMP UP THE VOLUME' (1990)
'ROBIN HOOD: PRINCE OF THIEVES' (1991)
'MOBSTERS' (1991)
'HERO WORSHIP' (1992)

Hobbies: Christian's a bit of a naughty boy and enjoys driving his swanky car at very high speed around Hollywood!

Friends: Christian's good mates with Sean Connery after they both appeared in 'The Name Of The Rose' together. He also hangs out with Charlie Sheen, but doesn't regard Kevin Costner as a chum after they fell out during the filming of 'Robin Hood: Prince Of Thieves'!

Lurve: Woo! Snogging is one of Christian's fave pastimes and he once snogged Winona Ryder! He can be seen out on the town with a different lady every weekend!

ROBERT DOWNEY JNR

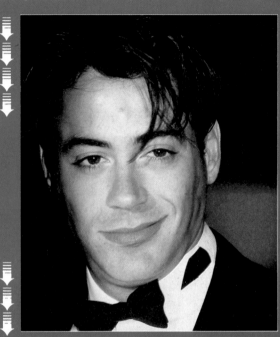

Born: 1965 in the USA.

What you've seen him in:
'POUND' (1970)
'GREASER'S PALACE' (1972)
'UP THE ACADEMY' (1980)
'BABY IT'S YOU' (1982)
'FIRSTBORN' (1984)
'WEIRD SCIENCE' (1985)
'TO LIVE AND DIE IN L.A.' (1985)
'TUFF TURF' (1985)
'BACK TO SCHOOL' (1986)
'THAT'S ADEQUATE' (1986)
'THE PICK-UP ARTIST' (1987)
'LESS THAN ZERO' (1987)
'JOHNNY BE GOOD' (1987)
'RENTED LIPS' (1987)
'1969' (1988)
'TRUE BELIEVER' (1988)
'CHANCES ARE' (1989)
'THREE OF HEARTS' (1989)
'AIR AMERICA' (1990)
'SOAPDISH' (1991)
'CHARLIE' (1992)

Hobbies: Robert used to be one of the wild young things in Hollywood and would party 'til he dropped, but now he's a clean-living, hard-working actor who hangs out on the beach.

Friends: After starring in 'Air America' with Mel Gibson the two became firm friends. He also chums around with Andrew McCarthy and Robert De Niro.

Lurve: Robert split up with long-time love Sarah Jessica Parker a while back and hasn't yet found a new love! He once snogged Madonna!

IN THE PINK

We're in for a long hot summer, so keep your cool in the prettiest of pinks.

SHADES OF SUMMER

Pink is the flirtiest of summer shades but also keep an eye open for baby blues, leaf green and — of course — white. These shades really do bring out the best in summer skins.

▼ Hat from The Hat Shop. Dress from Snob.

Cardigan from Freemans. Earrings from Stirling Cooper. ▶

MAKE-UP

When the heat is on your make-up invariably slides off, so keep it v. light. Indeedy, it's a good idea to use only mascara and lippy and let your skin breathe 'n' take in the beams, man.

BASE — We used a tinted moisturiser on our model which enhanced her natural skin tone, then gave it a perfect matt finish by pressing in a little translucent powder using a clean cotton wool ball.

EYES — V. simple this one — all we did was comb her eyelashes and give them an even coat of waterproof dark brown mascara — paying particular attention to her upper lashes which were given an extra coat. Her eyebrows were brushed and darkened a little using just a tad of the mascara (wipe off the excess with a tissue).

LIPS — This baby pink colour was applied with a lip brush, blotted then reapplied. The emphasis on this look was on the lips so make sure — when you do it at home — you do it perfectly!

SUMMER TIPS

● Choose natural fabrics like cotton (weave as well as the T-shirt variety), silk (or silk mixes), linen and wool (warm in winter, cool in summer). Synthetic fabrics won't absorb moisture and will make you feel clammy.

● During the hotter months, it's usually quite a temptation to get your hair cut short. Try tying it back, up, pulling it off your face with a hair band and plaiting. If you go for the chop you may regret it come the autumn.

● The sun can really damage your skin so whenever you're in the sun, slather on a generous amount of sunblock or a v. high protection factor over your face and neck. If the sun's strong, use a medium protection factor over the other bits of flesh on show!

● Your lips can become quite dry in the summer months, so be sure to keep them well protected with a S.P.F. 15 lip salve.

● If you've got a colour or a perm, the sun can play havoc with it. Look out for sun protective styling products and conditioners.

● Choose a waterproof mascara if you fancy a dip!

JACKIE **31**

SISTERLY LOVE!

A lucky short story by Judy Robinson.

It was the first time Francie's sister had taken her to a party and now it looked like she was going to mess it up . . .

WHEN she's angry, my sister turns a deep shade of purple. Most of the time I can't even work out what's annoyed her, but then older sisters are like that. Take the conversation at breakfast last Wednesday:

"His name's James and he's going to be a brain surgeon."

This was what Louise barked out when Mum asked, "Did you have a nice time at the party, dear?"

I couldn't for the life of me see the connection but I knew we were in for trouble.

"Mum, I know exactly what you mean. You try to ask casually but it's more like the Spanish Inquisition. I know very well you want to know if I met a suitable boy last night. I'm surprised you haven't already bought engagement party invitations.

"And so, that's why I'm telling you everything you need to know — his name's James and he's going to be a brain surgeon."

"Well, there's no need to be sarcastic, dear."

"I'm not. His name really is James."

"Louise, you know perfectly well what I mean. What is he training to be?"

"A brain surgeon, really."

She took a sip of coffee and smiled like I've only ever seen her smile when watching 'Top Gun'.

"And he's lovely."

I didn't have to wait long to meet this miracle worker, who'd changed my narky sister into a little angel.

The next Saturday, Louise wandered into my room and draped herself elegantly over my unmade bed.

"What are you up to tonight?" she asked, far too sweetly for my liking.

I chewed my bottom lip. "I'm just having an evening in."

"Well, not any more you're not. You're coming to the party with me!"

I grinned nervously — my brain was having a serious problem coping with the change from Louise, Queen of Darkness, to my Fairy Godmother.

Terrified

I was ready to go in 15 minutes flat. I washed my hair and even conditioned it, put on mascara and my new dress. Louise then spent another hour making me fit to be seen by the general public.

The party was in somebody's flat and we could hear the music right down the road. Louise for once seemed really nervous.

The place was packed like a sardine tin. Louise seemed to know everyone and introduced me to about eight million people all called Quentin or Tania — which was lucky because I wouldn't have remembered their names otherwise.

We'd made it to the kitchen, when a huge bloke who looked like a Sumo wrestler grabbed Lou from behind and twirled her round effortlessly with one finger.

If this was James, I was not overly impressed. Over-awed, yes. Terrified even. This boy had fingers the size of whole salamis — great for brain surgery, I don't think!

"Quentin!" Louise screamed in excitement as the mountainous being swept her away. I breathed again.

After 20 minutes standing in the kitchen trying to look enigmatic rather than just bored, I was pretty fed up.

On my third trip to the loo, I spent some time scrubbing my fingernails, colour coding the shampoo bottles on the side of the bath and trying to find an anagram for Freshmint Toothpaste.

Then someone started to hammer on the door and a voice shouted, "Are you planning to ever come out?"

I unlocked the door hurriedly, smiling in what I hoped was an apologetic manner. A boy was leaning right in the doorway, propped up on one arm with the other under his chin and his eyes shut, and pretended to wake up with a start when the door opened.

He was tall and thin with mousey brown hair that hung over his forehead. But he had a nice grin that made me smile back at him.

Then I spotted Louise in the hallway, clutching the arm of someone who looked distinctly like Andy Crane. When I turned back, the boy with the grin had disappeared into the bathroom.

After that I saw Louise about 20 times, but never got to speak to her. She kept whisking past, sometimes hot on the heels of the Andy Crane look-alike, who, I thought amazingly, must be James, the aspiring brain surgeon. Each and every time though, she didn't look very happy.

Then someone tapped me on the shoulder and I turned round.

"You're not really enjoying this, are you? You've spent most of the night either in the kitchen or locked up in the bathroom."

I bit my lip and looked up. For once he wasn't grinning and I had a strange feeling in my stomach.

His name was Jim and we talked for hours about nothing in particular but I didn't mind.

The only thing that niggled me occasionally, was Louise. I kept catching sight of her across the room, with her axe murderer's face on, glaring. Sometimes it even looked like she was glaring at me. But just one word from Jim and I'd forget all about her.

"Francie, would you come to the pictures tomorrow?"

"Yeah, I'd love to."

Then I remembered. "Oh, no, I've got to hand in a project on Monday and I . . . I suppose I could finish it during the day though. Yes, that'll be OK."

He laughed and squeezed my arm. "That's lucky. What are you studying for anyway?"

"I want to be a nurse. What about you?"

"Me? Oh, nothing much . . . I'm going to be a brain surgeon."

If only the ground had opened up and swallowed me! Across the room, Louise scowled murderously as I met her eyes. I don't remember how I got out, but I've never moved so quickly in my life.

The next morning, I heard Louise moving around in her room. At 10 o'clock she went downstairs and by half past, the smell of toast and coffee was driving me wild with hunger.

I sidled into the room and was just making myself a coffee when:

"Piece of toast, Francie?"

I nearly poured boiling water over my feet. "Er, er, yes please Lou."

"So, Mum, I've decided to finish with James. Apart from anything else, he hardly spoke to me all night. You saw that, didn't you, Francie?"

I turned deep red — Louise was talking to me.

"I mean, you must've noticed, Francie? You were there, after all. He hardly said a word to me, did he?"

I shook my head dumbly.

I had to get this sorted out before my brain short-circuited. I spoke slowly:

"So, so . . . was James, James the brain surgeon that is, the one who looked like Andy Crane?"

Laughter

Louise screamed — I flinched and waited for the blow — but it was with laughter. "Andy Crane? Oh, that's brilliant. Why didn't I notice before?"

I was a bit confused. If James was Andy, and Jim wasn't short for James, then who was Jim?

Louise didn't know who he was. "I kept coming up to talk to you but you seemed pretty engrossed, so I left you. Next thing I knew, you'd bolted for the door and were legging it down the road like Linford Christie."

By 6 o'clock, I'd worked myself into a deep depression at the thought of probably never seeing Jim again and was getting ready for a comforting pig-out in front of the telly, when the doorbell rang.

As I ran to answer it, my hands were shaking, but I hardly dared hope it could be him. It was.

"Hi."

"Hi."

"I wasn't sure if you still wanted to go out. You left in a bit of a rush. But . . . well, I thought I'd try anyhow. Was it something I said?"

"Well, sort of . . . Are you really going to be a brain surgeon?"

"I *thought* that was it. I couldn't understand it." He looked embarrassed. "Actually, I'm not. I was trying to be funny but you obviously didn't think so. I was going to tell you I was only joking, but you'd already disappeared."

He stopped. "So . . . is that it?"

I was so relieved I just laughed and nodded. "How did you find me?"

"Well, I asked, but no-one seemed to know you. Then this huge mountain of a person grabbed me by the neck. My life flashed before my eyes, but he introduced himself as Quentin, a friend of your sister, and gave me your address, so here I am."

"I'm glad."

"So, can I still take you out?"

"Do you still want to?"

"Of course, and I promise not to mention brains or surgery. I know it can make some people pretty queasy."

If only he knew.

Animal Magic!

Thinking of getting yourself a pet? Read on and find out everything you need to know!

Yippee! After years of ceaseless whingeing, moaning and griping, you've done it! You've been given the go-ahead to get a pet of your own! No doubt by this time there are Great Danes and panthers floating in front of your eyes, but slow down! There are one or two things to sort out first!

Where you live is a vital factor to consider when choosing a pet. If you live in a flat, there might be a No Dogs rule, so make sure you check that out before doing anything rash! Also, if you live in a built up area without a park for miles, getting a dog is a very bad idea.

Another thing you should think about carefully is the amount of time your pet will take up. If you're more interested in nights out at the old deesco than tramping round the park in the rain with your dog, maybe you'd better choose something which needs the minimum of care. You may think that something like a rabbit might not take much looking after, and compared to a dog, it doesn't — but they still need attention, and their cages still need cleaned.

Talk to a vet beforehand and find out how much your proposed pet will cost to keep and what sort of care it needs. There are usually various leaflets on display in the surgery which will be informative too.

Above all, before getting a pet, whether it's a goldfish or a Golden Retriever, make sure you're really serious about the venture. It wouldn't be fair on the animal (or your mum!) if you got fed up after a week or two!

DOGS

WHAT KIND?

The first thing to decide is what type of dog you want. If you live in a flat or small house or don't have spare hours every day to go for walks, then a small dog would be the best sort to get. But don't despair if you don't like Yorkies or Jack Russells — dogs like Spaniels, Beagles and Shetland Collies are all good flat-sized specimens!

WHERE CAN YOU GET YOUR DOG?

If your heart is set on a particular breed of pedigree dog, your best bet would be to get in touch with the Kennel Club. They should be able to give you the name of the breeder nearest you. Of course, there might not be a puppy available straight away, but you can book one.

Buying from an established breeder might work out a little more expensive, but it is worth it, as you'll find out the history of the pup's family, and if your dog turns out to be more than you can cope with, for whatever reason, they'll usually take it back.

If you like mongrels or just want to rescue an abandoned dog, the local dogs' home is the place to go. These animals need more care and understanding as they are often nervous because of earlier experiences.

WHAT TO ASK

A pup shouldn't really leave its mum until eight weeks, but the best age to get a puppy is at 12 weeks old, by which time it should be innoculated.

If the idea of toilet-training makes you feel sick, you can get an adult dog from the pound, or through ads in your local paper. Often people have to get rid of their pet through no fault of the dog's.

When you're buying your puppy, look for bright eyes, and an alert, interested expression. If the puppy is a mongrel, check the size of its paws — if they look big, the chances are the pup will grow into a big dog!

Feeding is very important so you should ask the breeder what he recommends. Don't be tempted to give your dog or puppy cow's milk, as they cannot digest it and it can damage their insides.

If you have little brothers or sisters, or the dog will be around children a lot, mention this to whoever you get the dog from! Some types of dog aren't good

they need hay to eat too, you might find it disappearing faster than you'd hoped!

Once you've bought your rabbit, take it to the vet for a check-up. The vet will be able to advise you about feeding, and he will also tell you if it's a boy or a girl, which could be well worth knowing if you're planning to get a companion for it!

EXOTIC PETS

SNAKES

The most important thing to have when buying a snake is a secure vivarium, as snakes leave Houdini standing when it comes to escapology!

Grass snakes make the best pets as they are friendly and easily tamed. Pythons and boas can also be kept, but they grow very big, and keeping them supplied with food is more of a problem. It is against the law to keep a poisonous snake as a pet.

A reputable supplier will help you choose a suitable pet snake which will give you lots of pleasure.

TARANTULAS

There are various types of giant spider, many of which are mistaken for tarantulas. Although most can bite, only a few are fatal, and those would never be offered for sale.

Enquiries at your pet shop would put you in touch with a stockist, so make sure you talk it through thoroughly with him before buying. Tarantulas eat live food like moths and insects, and are clean, quiet and placid creatures that make good pets.

with kids. Generally speaking, Labradors, Boxers, Bearded Collies and Samoyeds are very good-natured breeds.

CATS

Cats are more independent, laid-back dudes than dogs. They don't need exercise, which cuts down drastically the amount of time you have to set aside for them. However, they still need a lot of care and attention and there are different things to consider.

OUTDOOR OR INDOOR?

If you live in a quiet area and you have a garden, then you should be able to let your cat come and go as it pleases. But if you live in a busy area it might be safer to keep your cat in all the time. This means you'll have to teach your cat how to use a litter tray, but as they're naturally clean creatures, this isn't usually a problem.

BE SENSIBLE!

Any responsible cat owner will tell you as soon as it's old enough you should have your cat neutered. Tom cats have a charming habit of 'marking' their territory, and if that includes your duvet or dad's favourite chair — unlucky!

As for female 'outdoor' cats — a litter of kittens is almost guaranteed at some stage or other! And however appealing this might sound, there are *too many* unwanted cats in the world already! Don't add to the total by being irresponsible. If money's a bit tight in your house, The PDSA can help out by doing the operation for next to nothing!

WHERE CAN YOU GET A CAT?

Ads in the papers, pet shops or the Cats' Protection League are good places to start. The CPL are especially helpful as they will give you advice on practically everything! It might be a good plan to talk to them *before* you get your cat to find out exactly what's involved.

If you want a pedigree, the Governing Council of Cat Fancy, the 'Cats' Kennel Club' will be able to help.

RABBITS

Pet shops almost always have rabbits in stock, so getting hold of one shouldn't cause any trouble. However, it's a good idea to ask for advice before you buy your rabbit to make sure you're fully prepared!

A hutch is obviously the first priority, and the pet shop should be able to help you choose the right sort. You can bed your rabbit on sawdust or hay, but as

USEFUL ADDRESSES

The Kennel Club,
1 Clarges Street,
Piccadilly,
London W1.

Cats' Protection League,
17 Kings Road,
Horsham,
W. Sussex RH13 5PP.

The Governing Council of the Cat Fancy,
4-6 Penel Orlieu,
Bridgewater,
Somerset TA6 3PG.

The British Rabbit Council,
Purefoy House,
7 Kirkgate,
Newark,
Nottinghamshire.

GOLDE

Sigh! They don't make them like this anymore! Forget those youngsters of the silver screen and take a look at some classic crumblies.

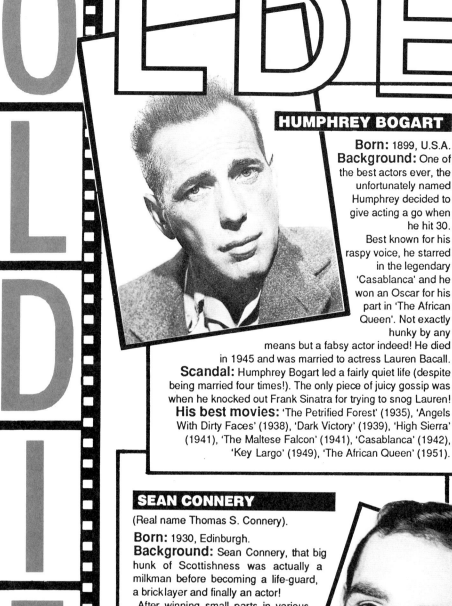

HUMPHREY BOGART

Born: 1899, U.S.A.
Background: One of the best actors ever, the unfortunately named Humphrey decided to give acting a go when he hit 30.
Best known for his raspy voice, he starred in the legendary 'Casablanca' and he won an Oscar for his part in 'The African Queen'. Not exactly hunky by any means but a fabsy actor indeed! He died in 1945 and was married to actress Lauren Bacall.
Scandal: Humphrey Bogart led a fairly quiet life (despite being married four times!). The only piece of juicy gossip was when he knocked out Frank Sinatra for trying to snog Lauren!
His best movies: 'The Petrified Forest' (1935), 'Angels With Dirty Faces' (1938), 'Dark Victory' (1939), 'High Sierra' (1941), 'The Maltese Falcon' (1941), 'Casablanca' (1942), 'Key Largo' (1949), 'The African Queen' (1951).

SEAN CONNERY

(Real name Thomas S. Connery).
Born: 1930, Edinburgh.
Background: Sean Connery, that big hunk of Scottishness was actually a milkman before becoming a life-guard, a bricklayer and finally an actor!
After winning small parts in various films he became Bond. James Bond! 'Dr No' was the first one in 1962.
He's since made seven more as the suave secret agent but is now just as well known for his parts in films like 'Highlander', 'Indiana Jones And The Last Crusade' and 'The Untouchables' (which won him an Oscar for best-supporting actor).
When he's not driving millions of women wild he plays golf!
Scandal: Big Sean's a genuine good guy, but takes no nonsense from anybody! He's been known to have had affairs with a few of his leading ladies, but is now happily married to his second wife, Micheline.
He's got one son Jason (also an actor) and a villa in Spain!
His best movies: 'Goldfinger' (1964), 'Marnie' (1964), 'The Man Who Would Be King' (1975), 'A Bridge Too Far' (1977), 'The Name Of The Rose' (1986), 'The Untouchables' (1987) and 'Indiana Jones And The Last Crusade' (1989).

PETER O'TOOLE

Born: 1932, Eire.
Background: The devilish Mr O'Toole left the Emerald Isle at an early age and was brought up in Leeds. Deciding that he'd rather be an actor than anything else, he got accepted for RADA and started making a name for himself in London plays.

After brief appearances in a few films he was signed up to play the lead in the now classic 'Lawrence Of Arabia' in 1962.

Lead roles soon followed and the saucy Peter appeared in 'How To Steal A Million', 'What's New Pussycat' and 'Goodbye Mr Chips' among others.

Most recently he returned to our screens in 'High Spirits' and 'King Ralph'.

Scandal: Peter was a bit of a wild one in his youth and liked nothing better than going out on the town with his acting chums, and snogging ladies! His best mate was Richard Burton and together they would have pretend sword fights with French loaves in restaurants!

Peter O'Toole's been married twice and has a son and a daughter.

His best movies: 'Lawrence Of Arabia' (1962), 'Lord Jim' (1964), 'What's New Pussycat' (1965), 'The Lion In Winter' (1968), 'Goodbye Mr Chips' (1969) and 'Under Milk Wood' (1971).

RICHARD BURTON

(Real name Richard Jenkins).

Born: 1925, Wales.
Background: Richard was the son of a miner and the 12th of 13 children. Since the Jenkins household was rather busy, he went off to live with his older sister.

While he was at high school, his English teacher persuaded him to take part in a school play — and the rest is, as they say, history!

He moved to London where he appeared in several plays and made his film debut in 'The Last Days Of Dolwyn' in 1948.

He was nominated for an Oscar seven times during his career but didn't win once. Richard Burton was a superb actor and starred in epics like 'Cleopatra', where he met his future wife Elizabeth Taylor (who he married twice!), 'Look Back In Anger' and 'The Desert Rats'. He died in 1984.

Scandal: Richard Burton was certainly one of the wild men of movies and could reduce his co-stars to tears with a few well-chosen words!

He would disappear from film sets for days on end and refused to act if his beloved Welsh rugby team had a game!

Richard Burton was married five times and had four children.

His best movies: 'My Cousin Rachel' (1952), 'Look Back In Anger' (1959), 'Cleopatra' (1963), 'The Night Of The Iguana' (1964), 'Who's Afraid Of Virginia Woolf?' (1966), 'Anne Of A Thousand Days' (1969) and 'Staircase' (1969).

GREGORY PECK

(Real name Eldred G. Peck).

Born: 1916, U.S.A.
Background: A bit of a 'dreamboat' when he was younger, Gregory Peck managed to get four Oscar nominations in six years!

He started out as a truck-driver but won a scholarship to acting school where he quickly landed a part in 'Days Of Glory'.

He was soon earning vast sums of money as a leading Hollywood actor and turning in fine performances in tons of films and winning an Oscar in 1963 for 'To Kill A Mockingbird'.

He's been married to the same woman for over 35 years and has a son.

Scandal: Gregory's life is scandal-free! Just as he mainly played good dependable chaps on screen — out of the movies he was a nice down to earth bloke, too!

His best movies: 'Spellbound' (1945), '12 O'Clock High' (1949), 'Roman Holiday' (1953), 'Moby Dick' (1956), 'The Big Country' (1958), 'The Guns Of Navarone' (1961), 'Cape Fear' (1962), 'How The West Was Won' (1962), 'To Kill A Mockingbird' (1963), and 'The Omen' (1976).

TOP OF THE CLASS

Fitting In

Whether you're starting a new school or even just a new class, there's bound to be a certain amount of worry and nervousness involved. When stepping into a new situation like that, you can often get the feeling that everyone has been let into some important secret . . . except you!

It's natural to feel nervous about new situations and even though things seem really big and new — you needn't think that you're completely out of your depth. It's important to remember that nearly everyone is, or has been, in exactly the same situation as you — so everyone knows how you'll be feeling.

Remember

● Try not to get too worried. It is hard, but there is absolutely no reason to get the whole thing out of proportion. Worrying yourself sick isn't going to help the situation at all.

● Even though you'll be feeling nervous — do your best to appear friendly and approachable. A smile and pleasant greeting is a lot more appealing than a look of terror!

● Listen carefully to everything you're told — even take notes if you have to. This way you can cut down on things that could worry you — like forgetting teachers' names or even where you are supposed to sit!

● Don't be tempted to laugh and carry-on to try to 'fit in'. You don't want to get into any trouble and just land a reputation as a joker — they're never taken seriously.

You spend five out of seven days of the week at school, so why not make the most of it?

Prep Time

Getting to school on time, complete with everything you need for the day can sometimes be a bit of a trial. Getting into the habit of preparing beforehand will help solve your problems.

● If you need a bus pass to get to school, check at the weekend if it's up-to-date or if it needs replaced. Don't leave it until you're in a mad rush for the bus on Monday morning . . . obviously, that's too late.

● When you get home from school at night is the best time to check your timetable and sort your bag out for the next day. Remember to look out all your books and folders — and if you've got P.E., check that you've got exactly the right equipment.

● Sort your uniform out the night before as well — this way even if you do sleep in, at least everything will be close to hand and in the same place. Scrabbling about for a pair of tights when the bus leaves in three minutes is never fun.

● The big horror — homework! No-one is fond of homework, but it has to be done, so get your hands

on a homework diary and take a note of what's to be done. Make sure you get a note of the right pages for the text books and exactly when it's to be handed in. The easiest way to keep ahead of homework is to simply try and get it all done the night you're actually given it.

A Class Act

No-one likes to admit when they don't understand something or if it's far too difficult for them . . . it doesn't help that teachers can seem a mite unapproachable at times. The only way to get round any classroom worries is to come clean and actually admit that you are 'stuck'.

OK, so you've re-read the book loads of times but things are still not making sense and you don't want to put your hand up in class and admit you don't understand in case everybody laughs. Don't be tempted to leave things as they are and remain in ignorance. Instead, you could wait after class and admit to your teacher that you don't understand. Your teacher will be only too pleased to help. After all, they are there to help you learn! If you really feel that you can't approach your teacher, maybe you

could go and see your form teacher and ask them to act on your behalf. Alternatively, you could also chat to your mum and dad about it and they could get in touch with the school to chat about any problems you are having.

Testing Testing

Exams looming on the horizon are never very funny. But, there's

no need to get uptight about them. Just organise yourself with a study timetable and stick to it. If you're sure of your facts 'n' figures, there will be no need to worry.

The start of the term, even though the exams seem really faraway, is really the best time to get started. Every night, for about half an hour or so, sit down and go over everything you did that day and have a look at any notes you've made. If there are any you don't understand, ask your teacher about it the next time you're in their class.

As the exams get nearer, work out a simple study timetable — allow yourself to study one subject a night — for example, Maths on a Monday, English on a Tuesday. Studying too many subjects in one night will just muddle your head and you won't take anything in . . . or manage to get some decent sleep!

If you study over a longer period of time, when it comes to the stage just before your exams,

you'll find all you really need to do is some revision and brushing up.

School-Type Tips

● Don't fall into the trap of laughing and chatting all through your classes. It may seem like fun at the time, but the fun should really be kept for breaks and for after school.

● Try not to get mixed up in the wrong crowd. Although some people might seem rebellious and interesting, it's a pretty short-term attraction. Your education is one of

the basic groundings for what you'd like to do in life — is it really worth wasting?

● Never be tempted to play truant. We might sound 'soft', but you and your parents could end up in serious trouble. If there is some sort of problem that's stopping you from going to school, go and see someone about it. The sooner you stop avoiding things and confront them — the sooner they work out.

● Although school is a fabsy place to meet boys, try to keep the romances out of the classroom. Dwelling too much on lads means there's bound to be a lack of concentration during lessons.

WORK THAT BODY

Weight Training

It's time to get fit with our guide to what's best in exercise...

If you want to end up with muscles like Arnie then this is the sport for you. But remember to take it easy to begin with!

You can use either free weights or weight machines and they're all designed to work on specific parts of the body. You'll probably notice that rather than actually losing weight you'll be losing inches. Fat is burned off and muscles are built up. Don't be alarmed if you're actually putting on weight because muscle weighs twice as much as fat.

You should start off using light weights and a few repetitions working up to heavier weights and more repetitions as you get stronger and fitter. Weight training burns off about 200-250 calories per half an hour. For working out you should wear either loose clothing or clingy Lycra depending on which you prefer. Don't wear anything that could restrict your movement.

Weight training can be a bit boring so think about taking a Walkman while you're working out.

Tennis

...favourite summer sport that can be ...ore enjoyable by watching all those hunky ...en bounding round the court in their ...nnis whites! It concentrates on the upper ...d lower parts of your body and as you ...t better the more physically demanding it ...n become, burning around 200 calories ...r half an hour. As well as being a good ...ort for your muscles, tennis also ...proves your co-ordination. So even if you ...end more time picking the ball up than ...tting it during your first session, you'll get ...ch better as time goes on.

...Wear a pair of loose shorts and a T-shirt ...d a pair of all-purpose trainers. If you ...cide you want to play regularly a pair of ...oper trainers would be a good buy. Don't ...orry about a racket and balls as sport ...ntres will be able to hire them out to you.

Jogging

This may seem just too much like hard work but done properly it can be very beneficial and enjoyable.

The most important thing to remember is, don't just rush out and start jogging. A few warm-up exercises will help you a lot. A sensible way to start is to walk and jog — five minutes walking, five minutes jogging and so on building up slowly to jogging all the time. Eventually, you should be aiming for about 30 minutes jogging every day which will burn off about 200 calories. Wear loose clothing and a pair of proper running shoes is essential. A bad pair of trainers can cause loads of damage to your spine and cause very bad back problems. Don't go jogging when it's dark and stick to busy places such as parks during the day and streets you know well.

Never wear a Walkman as it can prevent you from hearing all sorts of things. Make sure you're as safe as you can be.

Cycling

For a start, it's a lot easier than jogging because at least you're sitting down! Although cycling will eventually benefit your whole body you'll notice the difference in your legs to begin with, especially your calves and thighs. Not only that, but it's also brilliant for your heart and lungs because of all the oxygen pumping round your body. Aim to cycle for about 30 minutes every day and remember to keep a steady pace. You don't want to burn yourself out after five minutes! You should burn off about 300 calories per session. Any old bike will do as long as it's the correct height. And if you don't fancy cycling outside why not think about an exercise bike? They have exactly the same benefits except you don't go anywhere! Your clothing should be loose to allow you to move freely and invest in a pair of all-purpose trainers.

Swimming

Swimming's a great sport for every part of your body and because you're being supported by the water it's one of the easiest and most relaxing (unless you're planning on thrashing the water to a foam, that is!).

It gives you a cardiovascular workout, which concentrates on the heart and lungs, and it especially strengthens the arms, legs and upper body. You can expect to burn about 250 calories every 30 minutes. It's an ideal sport for people with a bad back because of the support you get from the water.

You'll need a swimming costume which is designed for swimming and not for lazing around on the beach. But there are some really nice colours and styles around just now so you won't have to look like you're having a school swimming lesson. They won't break the bank, either!

DREAMY FACTS

* You don't always remember them, although you dream every night.
* You can recall your dreams if you tell yourself before you sleep that you must remember them when you waken up.
* Before you go to sleep, think about one of these images: a gold cross, a tree, a bird in flight . . . they're supposed to lead you into the Land of Dreams!
* Did you know that the idea for sewing machines, canned food and even the atomic bomb came from dreams first?
* During sleep, problems, fears and hopes are viewed differently than when you're awake. So, the next time you've got a problem and someone tells you to 'sleep on it', listen to them, it's good advice!
* The sleeping mind does not communicate in words, it uses scenes, actions and symbols and this is the language we must learn if the dream is to be understood. So let's suss out a few of the most common ones . . .

DREAM ON

Did you know that your dreams can reveal your problems, fears and hopes for the future? No? Well, read on for some crucial info on dreaming . . .

ACORNS: You're a lucky lass if you've dreamt about acorns, these indicate tremendous success and a happy family for the future too!

APPLES: To dream that you're eating an apple means a bit of a disappointment is in store for you. But, don't worry 'cos if you throw away the pips good things will happen soon!

BANANAS: As with all other fruits, it means you're about to receive a lucky windfall.

BLUSHING: Oh-oh . . . what've you been up to?! You're feeling guilty about something!

CATS: To dream of a black cat is very lucky indeed!

CHERRIES: A warning dream . . . you'll be tempted to make a move on your mate's boyfriend!

CLIMBING: To climb stairs, hills or mountains shows that you're having a hard time, but don't worry 'cos things can only get better!

CLOWNS: Beware of making a fool of yourself!

DAISIES: Aww . . . you ol romantic! This is a symbol of lov affection and kindness.

FALLING: This means you're feelin insecure and also embarrasse about something.

FLAMES: Oo-er . . . beware of bein too passionate!

FLOWERS: This means that lov and friendship are about t blossom for you.

FORESTS: Don't be fooled by false friend.

FROGS: You're in the mood for total change of image.

HATS: You're a dreamer and yo want to be admired by everyone.

ICE: Ooh . . . watch out, you'r becoming just a bit cold-hearted.

JEWELLERY: You're so vain — sto trying too hard to attract attentio to yourself.

Follow these fab tips and you'll be feelin' fit in no time!

get healthy!

* Eat plenty . . . of what's good for ya! Don't diet — just switch to healthier options. For instance, instead of sugary fizzy drinks buy the under one calorie variety, fresh orange juice or mineral water; instead of chips have a baked potato; instead of choccy have some luscious fruit. Mmm . . . fabsy.

* Get out 'n' about. Sitting in watching the telly really does give you a flabby belly so do something. Go skating, bowling, walking in the park, join the volleyball club or tap dancin' classes. The more fun 'n' games you get up to the better 'n' healthier you'll feel.

* Come the warmer months take real care of your skin in the sun. Wear a sunblock if you're prone to burning, and don't stay out in the sun for hours at a time, especially around lunch-time when the beams are at their baddest!

* Be sure you get your teeth checked every six months and make use of free dental care while you can!

* No matter how big and clever you think it is, smoking is bad news. It makes you smell, gives you bad breath, severely damages your lungs and costs a fortune.

* Always get plenty of sleep. On average eight hours is what's advised but you may find you need more or even less. On school nights you ought to be in the land of nod by 11 pm at t'latest!

* Promise yourself you're going to take better care of your skin. We know, we say it almost every week, CLEANSE, TONE and MOISTURISE morning and night. It only takes a few minutes and you really do notice a difference. Give yourself a weekly facial scrub and face mask too — this'll keep dry skin and spots at bay.

* Buy some new sports gear an trainers. They'll make you fee like doing some kind of exercise. Check out your loc leisure centre to see what they've got to offer — talent wise too!

NOCKING: Prepare yourself for a irrova shocka . . . something big s about to happen.

AUGHTER: A happy sign, but try to ugh at yourself more than others.

IERMAID: A sad dream, meaning our bloke's just chucked you. But on't worry, someone else is oming your way soon.

IOON: Don't be too possessive ith your bloke . . . he won't like it!

UMBERS: You're panicking about II of the schoolwork you've got.

RCHIDS: You're about to meet a andsome, passionate bloke!

ARROTS: You talk too much!

ARTIES: Your social life is about to hange for the better.

ADIOS: Expect a telepathic essage!(?)

AIN: A good sign, all of your orries and troubles will soon isappear.

OSES: True love will be yours for ver.

UNNING: You may be running owards something, or running way from something you won't ace.

HEEP: Don't be easily led.

TARS: Someone you know is bout to have a baby.

HUNDER: Watch out, you're going o get hassle from a teacher at chool.

VASP: A friend will betray you.

ODIAC: You'll achieve fame and ortune . . . lucky thing!

*So there you have it.
Happy dreaming!*

Think positive and be happy!

model file

If you've ever fancied being a model read on and find out what it's really like!

NAME: NICOLA HOLMES

AGE: 17

HEIGHT: 5' 9"

WEIGHT: 8st 8lbs.

How did you get into modelling, Nicola?
I had a friend who was a model and she suggested I go to her agency so I went along and they took me on!

What type of jobs have you done?
Mainly editorial (beauty, fashion) for magazines. I've also done catwalk shows, some TV and advertising work.

What are the good points about modelling?
Well, having the opportunity to travel and getting paid to do it! Also, it's different from a normal nine to five job 'cos the hours are always different.

Any bad points?
Relying on public transport to get me round London in time for my appointments!

What do your friends think about it all?
It's taken a bit of getting used to, I think, but now they know what the business is like, they don't think it's glamorous at all!

What about diet and exercise — do you do it?
Well, I do exercises — I've always enjoyed sport anyway, but I'm afraid dieting is hopeless where I'm concerned! I just can't stop eating!

Any beauty tips that you'd swear by?
Start the day with a refreshing shower and always follow a cleanse, tone and moisturise routine for clear skin.

What's your essential fashion item?
Definitely black leggings, 'cos I can team them with so many types of clothes for loads of different looks.

Any advice to readers who want to be models?
If you really want to be a model don't part with any cash especially for getting a portfolio of photographs done. Just visit reputable agencies and if they think you have any potential they will arrange for you to be photographed professionally without it costing you a penny!

1. Read all your old Jackie annuals and have a larf at the haircuts and the popstrels of long ago! Five Star? Who?

2. Get together all the clothes you're bored with and won't wear again, get your mates to do the same, and have a gear-swopping party! You could end up with some rad new outfits!

3. Arrange a night out with a mate and spend all day getting ready! Dig out all your Body Shop Christmas goodies, book the bathroom for five hours, and really go to town!

4. Take up something you've always wanted to learn. Can you swim, or d'you fancy making your own 'threads'? Book lessons today!

5. Get a few mates together, pool all your cash towards loadsa videos, popcorn and crisps, and slob out!

6. Dig out all your old diaries and reminisce over the larfs and tears of yesteryear!! (And the lads, of course!)

7. Work out a whole new diet and exercise programme for yourself. Eat healthy meals (lots of fresh fruit and veggies) and haul yourself out for a walk or even a run (!) every day. You'll soon feel so good you'll have forgotten what being blue feels like!

8. Write your own 'True Experience'! Use something that really happened to you — then send it in to Jackie! We might even print it!

9. Give your best friend a make-over in the style of her fave pop star, then get her to do the same for you.

10. Give your feet a treat! A good long soak in the tub and a pedicure will leave your tootsies tingling!

11. Change your bedroom around and have a good clear-out at the same time. You'll find things you'd forgotten you ever had!

12. Have a do-it-yourself karaoke evening! Make your mates get up and sing along with all your favourite discs! (You'll have to do it too, remember!)

50 WAYS
TO BEAT
THE BLUES

Put a smile back on your face with this lot!

3. Go shopping! Even if you haven't any money, you and your mates can have a great time trying on loadsa gear!

4. Get yourself a penpal! Write off to a few addresses in your weekly copy of Jackie and it might be the start of a beautiful friendship!

5. Spend an hour or so imagining what you would do if your fairy godmother gave you a big batch of 'wonga'!

6. Devise a plan of action to grab the lad you've been mooning after for months!

7. Clean out that filthy old make-up bag and re-stock it!

8. Sit down with yer favourite book, a big bar o' choccie, and relax!

9. Watch 'Pretty Woman'. Awww!

10. Get hold of as many newspapers and magazines as you can, arm yourself with a dictionary and a clever relation, and enter all the competitions you can — you might win a fortune!

11. Treat yourself to a fab new hair-do. Have a chat with the stylist first to get some ideas, and you'll come out feeling great!

22. Join Amnesty International, or a Green organisation. You'll feel you're doing something useful!

23. Write to all the people you haven't been in touch with for a while.

24. Dig out all your old records, clean them, and catalogue them!

25. Take your dog for a long walk on the beach or in the park. That'll blow the 'cobwebs' away! (If you don't have a dog, borrow one!)

26. Do a good deed for the day and feel all virtuous!

27. Read the problem page of a magazine — you're bound to find someone feeling worse than you!

28. Make a big chocolate cake — then eat it!

29. Go to your local park and have a swing!

30. Dig out the ol' family photo album, ask your mate to bring hers, and scream with laughter at all the old piccies!

31. Experiment with your make-up and find yourself a new look.

32. Dig out all your old games, like Cluedo and Snakes 'n' Ladders and spend an afternoon playing them with your mates.

33. Trot down to your local newsagent's and place an order for Jackie every week!

34. Break open your piggy bank and treat yourself to some pretty underwear! Guaranteed to make you feel better!

35. Go down to the library and borrow the books you used to read when you were little. Famous Five ahoy!

36. Brighten up your hair with a semi-permanent colour!

37. Get yourself down to the local disco and dance till you drop!

38. Write letters to all the people you don't like telling them exactly what you think of them. Then rip 'em up, quick!

39. Listen to 'Don't Worry, Be Happy' by Bobby McFerrin.

40. Watch every episode of 'Blackadder'. If that doesn't get you laughing, nothing will!

41. Write down your top 10 'reasons to be cheerful'!

42. Phone up your best friend and have a girlie chat!

43. Persuade your mum to let you have a party and invite all the boys you fancy!

44. Write down all your favourite jokes so you never forget them!

45. Go to visit your granny!

46. Find out if there are any pantomimes still running near you, and go along and act like a six-year-old. "Look behind yooo!"

47. Treat yourself to the ultimate fashion accessory — a hat! You'll feel jolly classy!

48. Buy a present for yer mum! That'll make you feel great!

49. Go down to yer local department store and test all the expensive perfumes! Poo!

50. Design yourself a new outfit — who knows, you might even find someone who'll make it up for you!

BRAIN BENDER

Why not escape from boring old TV and try our star quiz!

OLD TIMERS!

Ask an old 'un for help in this section!

1) Liza Minelli recorded an album with the Pet Shop Boys — who was her mom, who starred in 'The Wizard Of Oz'?

2) What was Elvis Presley's middle name?

3) This 70's supergroup hailed from Scotland and were fond of wearing tartan flares 'n' massive platforms — who were they?

4) This group soared to the top of the charts in 1991 with 'Should I Stay Or Should I Go' after it appeared in a Levi's ad, 15 years after they were the leaders of the punk movement — see pic.

5) Name all four members of The Beatles.

GIRL TALK!

1) 'Baby Love' and 'Love And Kisses' were two big hits for this saucy lass — who is she?

2) Madonna's documentary was called 'In Bed With Madonna' over here, but what was it called in her home country?

3) This dumpy Scouse singer had a hit with 'Be Young, Be Foolish, Be Happy' — who is she?

4) What was Kim Appleby's first so hit?

5) This girl sang about her 'Emotions' and she's oft' been compared to Whitney Houston — who are we talking about?

DOUBLE ACTS!

These chaps and chapesses starred in movies together recently — name the stars and the movies!

1) He's married to Demi Moore, starred in 'Die Hard' and doesn't have much hair.
   She appeared briefly in 'St Elmo's Fire', starred in saucy 'Sex, Lies And Videotape' and snogged big conk Gerard Depardieu in 'Green Card'.

2) This girl was also in 'St Elmo's Fire', used to go out with Emilio Estevez and had a very public pregnancy.
   The lad is a bit of a dirty dancer, he's married to Lisa Niemi and he owns a ranch!

3) He's a bit of a 'Cry Baby', he used to work at '21 Jump Street' and his fingers were rather sharp in this movie.
   She's snogged Rob Lowe and Dennis Quaid on screen, she's chums with Cher and she's the real-life lover of her co-star in this film.

4) He's a Buddhist who's also 'An Officer And A Gentleman', and he was the baddie in 'Internal Affairs'.
   She was once caught 'Sleeping With The Enemy', which is what Kiefer Sutherland found out when she went out with Jason Patric!

5) She was a Southern belle in 'Shag', she fought a few 'Gremlins' and she's married to Kevin Kline.
   He used to be a 'Young One', he showed his 'Bottom' on TV and he's also a 'New Statesman'.

A BUNDLE OF BLOKES!

Name three of the four 'lobsters'.

Who was Kurt Russell's fire-fighting bruv in 'Backdraft'?

What was the name of Linda Hamilton's cute son in 'Terminator 2'?

4) Who was the delectable chap who snogged Milla Jovovich in 'Return To The Blue Lagoon'?

In 'Toy Soldiers', the star of 'Stand By Me' got together with one of 'The Goonies' — name them.

MALE CROONERS!

1) Harry Connick Jnr has made quite a few albums where he's tinkling on the old joanna, but which wartime film did Harry star in as a piano-playing airman?

2) Which New Kid crooned the 'classic' 'Treat Me Right' on their debut album?

3) Marc Almond's had a few hits on his own, but which chart-topping duo did he front in the early 80's?

4) Who was number one in 1991 for about 986 weeks with '(Everything I Do) I Do It For You'?

5) Paul Young had a hit called 'Sensa Una Donna' with an Italian geezer — what was the continental chap's name?

SEQUEL SECTION!

Milla Jovovich was stranded in paradise in 'Return To The Blue Lagoon' — who was the female star of 'The Blue Lagoon', original version?

2) "Hasta La Vista, Baby" — which sequel is this line taken from?

3) Which British female singer met a watery end in 'Lethal Weapon 2'?

4) True or false: the inevitable disaster to occur in 'Die Hard 2' happened in an airport.

5) William Ragsdale starred in 'Mannequin On The Move' — who was the male star of the original?

ANSWERS

Male Crooners!
1) 'Memphis Belle'
2) Joe McIntyre
3) Soft Cell
4) Bryan Adams
5) Zucchero

Sequel Section!
1) Brooke Shields
2) Terminator 2'
3) Patsy Kensit
4) True
5) Wil Wheaton and Sean Astin

A Bundle Of Blokes!
1) Richard Grieco, Costas Mandylor, Christian Slater or Patrick Dempsey
2) Billy Baldwin
3) Edward Furlong
4) Brian Krause
5) Chapess — Phoebe Cates Film — 'Drop Dead Fred'

Old Timers!
1) Judy Garland
2) Aaron
3) Bay City Rollers
4) The Clash
5) John Lennon, Paul McCartney, George Harrison, Ringo Starr

Girl Talk!
1) Dannii Minogue
2) 'Truth Or Dare'
3) Sonia
4) 'Don't Worry'
5) Mariah Carey

Double Acts!
1) Chap — Bruce Willis Chapess — Andie McDowell Film — 'Hudson Hawk'
2) Chap — Patrick Swayze Chapess — Demi Moore Film — 'Ghost'
3) Chap — Johnny Depp Chapess — Winona Ryder Film — 'Edward Scissorhands'
4) Chap — Richard Gere

Chapess — Julia Roberts Film — 'Pretty Woman'
5) Chap — Rik Mayall

LOVE MATCH?

LATER . . .

MAYBE LYNN AND SHONA ARE RIGHT. I REALLY LIKE FOOTBALL, BUT SOMETIMES I WOULDN'T MIND GOING OUT WITH SOMEONE WHO COULD TALK ABOUT SOMETHING DIFFERENT FOR A CHANGE . . .

ALLIE, THERE'S SOMEONE ON THE PHONE FOR YOU.

HE SAYS HIS NAME'S PETE . . .

OK, COMING. WHO IS IT?

HI ALLIE, IT'S PETE.

OH — ER, HI, PETE.

LISTEN, I WAS WONDERING WHETHER YOU FANCIED GOING OUT SOMETIME . . . I MEAN, IF YOU'RE NOT DOING ANYTHING ELSE . . .

YEAH, THAT'D BE REALLY NICE. WHERE DO YOU WANT TO GO?

I'VE GOT A COUPLE OF TICKETS FOR THE MATCH ON WEDNESDAY. I THOUGHT WE COULD GO TO THAT.

OH, NO, SORRY I CAN'T ON WEDNESDAY.

OH, RIGHT . . . WELL, WHAT ABOUT THE GAME ON SATURDAY?

NO, I DON'T THINK SO . . . LOOK, I'VE GOT TO GO. SEE YOU.

BRILLIANT. WHEN SOMEONE FINALLY DOES ASK ME OUT ALL THEY WANT TO DO IS GO TO A FOOTBALL MATCH. THERE MUST BE SOMEONE OUT THERE WHO ISN'T JUST INTERESTED IN FOOTBALL . . .

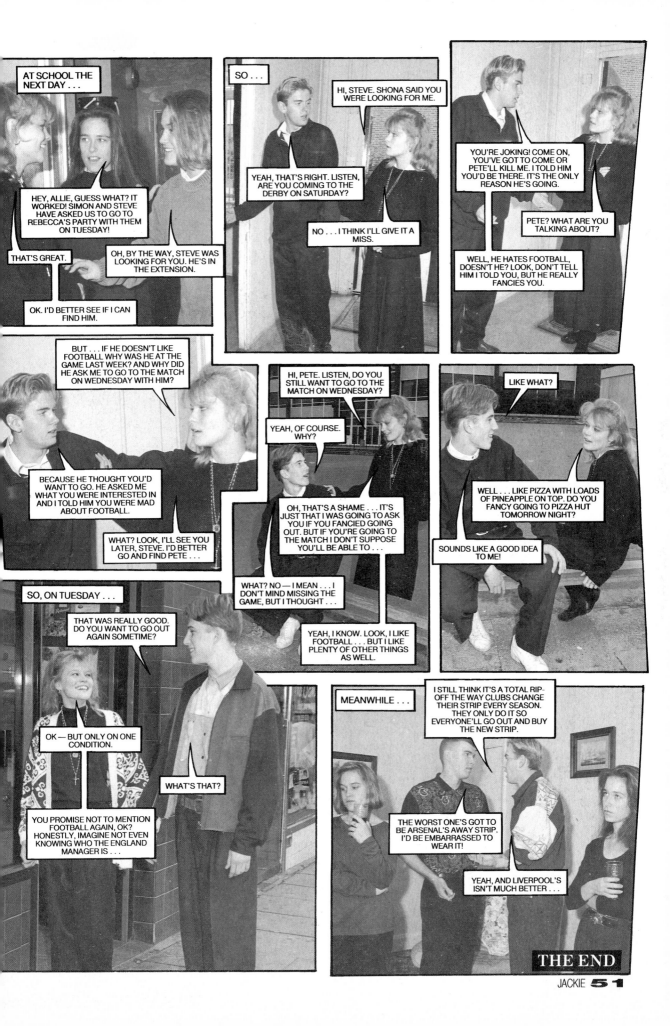

If you're fed up with people asking what you want to do when you leave school, and you haven't a clue, don't despair! We can help, with some great ideas for working girls!

Shots: Martin at Upfront. Thanks to the Royal Alexander Hospital.

ADMINISTRATION

Lesley, 23, Jackie, 24 and Charlotte, 22 all work in Hospital Administration.

What's working in Hospital Administration all about?
Lesley: "My job is to enter all the data my boss gives me into the computer. I keep records of his special projects about the hospital. I'm his personal secretary, I do everything for him from arranging appointments to sending out letters."
Jackie: "I work in the eye clinic. It's my job to make appointments, answer the phone and answer queries. I make sure everything runs smoothly in the department."
Charlotte: "I work in reception, making appointments and dealing with phone calls. I also keep medical records up to date and deal with case sheets going to wards. I have to make sure every doctor has all the required information on his patient."

What qualifications do you need for the job?
Lesley: "A good knowledge of computers and word-processing is essential. A good pass in Secretarial Studies is an advantage."
Jackie: "You've also got to be quite outgoing to deal with the public and you must be very patient."

What do you like best about your job?
Lesley: "I like the fact that the day goes by really quickly. I'm always busy and I really like the people here. There's a great atmosphere."
Jackie: "I like the fact that I work in a hospital. You feel you're doing something worthwhile."

G GIRLS

VETERINARY NURSE

Julie is 19 and in her second year of training to be a veterinary nurse.

What qualifications did you need, Julie?

"You need at least 4 'O' levels, including Maths and a science. In Scotland, you have to work 35 hours a week in a practice, and go to college in the evenings or on day release. In England, you work for one year in a practice with 3 months' block release. The training is 2 years minimum and you have to be at least 17.

"In order to be accepted, you must look for a post in a practice which is registered. That's very important."

Didn't you want to be a vet rather than a nurse?

"Well, yes, I did, but you need 5 Higher passes all at A, or 3 'A' Levels — all taken at one sitting! But now I've been a nurse, I wouldn't change."

What does your job involve?

"Everything! Cleaning, stocktaking, ordering drugs, preparing animals for surgery, assisting in operations, post-surgical care, reception duties, helping with X-rays — you name it, we do it!"

How did you feel the first time you saw an operation?

"It didn't bother me — I was too interested in what was going on!"

What sort of person do you have to be to do this job?

"You have to be very patient — with the animals *and* the vets! You have to be able to accept responsibility, but you must also recognise where your responsibility stops and the vet's takes over. Obviously you can't be at all squeamish, and you must be able to control your emotions. If an owner sees *you* going to pieces when their pet is getting put to sleep, what chance do they have?

"It also helps to be sympathetic and outgoing as a nurse's job involves a lot of client handling."

What's the worst part of the job?

"The cleaning, I think. Everything has to be cleaned

Thanks to Julie and the Parkside Vet Group.

every day, whether it's been used or not. I don't mind cleaning something that's dirty, but it's a bit of a bore cleaning things that are already clean!"

And the best part?

"Oh, the animals! It's great to see a dog or something that came in ill go out healthy again!"

WORKING GIRLS • WORKING GIRLS • WORKING GIRLS • WORKING GIRLS • WORKING GIF

MIDWIFE

Pauline, 25, has just qualified as a midwife.

Entrance qualifications: vary from college to college but most include English and a science, preferably at higher level.

What is involved in midwifery?

"We learn to look after the woman before she has her baby. We go to labour wards and deliver babies. We also work in special care units with tiny babies in incubators, and we work in post natal wards, teaching women how to look after themselves and their babies. We work in the community and in clinics as well — we spend five months at a time in ante/post natal, community areas and baby wards. This is good because it keeps you up to date, there are radical changes going on in the profession and it's becoming very research-based. Once you're qualified you're still studying and learning."

Is there a typical day as a midwife?

"No, there isn't really. I like the variation but I'd really prefer to stay in baby care."

What kind of person do you have to be for this job?

"You have to be able to communicate with people, to be understanding, eager and motivated. Interested in your career, basically. And absolutely *not* squeamish when it comes to labour, you have to be calm under pressure."

Are there any drawbacks to this job?

"Shift work. If there is a drawback — that's it! We work from 2 a.m.-10 a.m. and then 7.45 p.m.-2.45 a.m. the next morning. But that's nursing for you, you've got to be prepared for that."

Best thing about being a midwife?

"Seeing mums with their new babies, that's really satisfying. If you've been sitting with someone through eight hours in labour and she has this baby at the end of it, that's wonderful!"

What advice would you give to young girls thinking about a career in midwifery?

"If you want to be a midwife there's a diploma course which is the best way to learn. Go for it, if that's what you want."

KENNEL MAID

Caroline is 16 and works at a kennel which has both boarders and show dogs.

Did you need experience for the job, Caroline?

"Not really — you learn as you go along. After I've trained for two years I'll be a qualified kennel maid."

Describe a typical day.

"None of our days are typical! Normally I deal with the German Shepherds, the show dogs, feeding, grooming, cleaning the kennels and so on. But if the owner, Mrs Black, is away to a show or something, then I have to see to the boarders, too.

"Then there are always new dogs coming in, so I have to deal with the public as well."

What have you learned since coming to work at the kennels?

"Oh, all sorts of things! Feeding and nutrition are especially important, and I've learned a lot about that! Also, I've learned about rearing puppies, and how to split up a dog fight. In fact, it's quite scary how little you do know until you come to a place like this!"

Have you ever been bitten?

"One of the boarders once took a hold of me and didn't want to let go! I couldn't yell for help because that would have made her panic, so I just had to wait until she got fed up!"

How do you handle nervous dogs?

"If the dog is nervous or growling, I generally just go into the kennel and sit down! If the dogs can approach you in their own time, they're usually fine."

Thanks to Happas Zaandam Kennels.

What's the best thing about the job?

"It must be learning all about the dog behaviour. And I love seeing the puppies growing up!"

And the worst?

"Washing the beds — it's never ending!"

What do you want to do in the future?

"I want to be a professional dog handler, and be able to help people train their dogs properly. The same sort of thing as Mrs Black does, actually! I'd love to have a place like this one day!"

PHARMACY TECHNICIAN

Leslie, 20 and Linda, 21 have both been qualified for a year.

What was involved in your training?

Leslie: "It was mostly chemistry we studied throughout the two years of the course. The 1st Year isn't really related to the job, it was mainly lab safety and micro biology."

Linda: "You learn a lot about the technique involved in making up syrups, etc. The course is a series of modules and you're continually assessed."

Describe what being a Pharmacy Technician is about.

Leslie: "Well, we rotate around four or five departments, which is good because it's not boring. Working in the wards, what we do is order all of the drugs and external dressings that the hospital uses. We keep an eye on the stock every day and keep a note of what's been used."

Linda: "We make up a lot of nutrition for the really sick patients who can't take anything by mouth. We also make up IU additives which are antibiotics, which saves the doctor having to make them up."

Leslie: "This is done in a sterile environment so you have to get gowned-up to work there. Sometimes you have to get changed three times in one day!"

Could you describe a typical day as a Pharmacy Technician?

Linda: "I'm working on prescriptions this week, which is making up and ordering everything the department needs for two days. I'm told what's needed and it's my job to make sure they get it. Then I work on the wards and top up all of the drugs and dressings. I spend a lot of time working on the computer where I keep a record of all the medication used."

Leslie: "I'm working a lot with the dermatology unit at the moment, so I get lots of creams and ointments to make up. This is all done in a sterile area."

Why did you decide to become a Pharmacy Technician?
Leslie: "The careers guidance teacher recommended it to me at school, so I went for it. I'm glad I did — it's an interesting job and you meet lots of people."
Linda: "I saw the job advertised and thought it sounded good. It's a good way to use your knowledge of chemistry."

What type of person do you have to be for this job?
Linda: "You have to be strong enough to cope with some of the sights you see in the wards. You can't show any disgust at all."
Leslie: "It's really important to like chemistry, and to enjoy working with people. Again, you can't show any emotions at all and be able to apply yourself to everything you do. Sometimes

you're thrown in at the deep end so you've got to keep calm and muddle through using everything you've learned."

Leslie: "The wages and lack of holidays. Apart from that, it's a great job."
Linda: "I think the worst thing is the lack of promotion. Once you're qualified it's really difficult to work your way up to a senior post."

What do you like most about your job?
Linda: "The varied day because I'm never bored."
Leslie: "I like it because it's exciting and you never quite know what's going to happen next."

What advice would you give to young girls who fancy a career in pharmacy?
Leslie: "I'd say that if you have the qualifications to go on and become a pharmacist. They get paid wads more!"
Linda: "I think it's important to study hard, I thought school was a big joke and I regret that. Make sure you've got good qualifications before you leave."

WORKING GIRLS • WORKING GIRLS • WORKING GIRLS • WORKING GIRLS • WORKING G

STABLE-HAND

Clare is 18 and works at a riding school.

What does a normal day involve, Clare?
"Well, we start work at eight, but because I have my own horse to tend to, I start at seven! We feed all the horses and ponies, then muck out and clean up the yard. I take the beginners' lessons, then we groom the ponies and sort out the tack. After lunch, we tack up ready for the rides, and take the rides out. If it's too wet to go out, we clean all the tack. Then the horses get bedded down for the night and fed."

Do you need experience before a stable will take you on?
"It depends. I could hardly ride at all when I started my last job. The best thing to do is start going to the riding school, take lessons, find out how things get done there. If you're familiar with the yard and its routine you stand a better chance."

Have you ever been hurt in the course of your work?
"I've fallen off, but that's all so far! I've seen people being run over by horses, though."

What sort of person do you have to be to do this job?

"You have to be prepared to work hard, and I suppose it helps if you're fit! You have to be patient, and good with people as well as animals, because there's a lot of dealing with the public."

What's the best part of the job?
"Seeing yourself improve, and getting more out of your horse."

And the worst?
"Getting up in the morning and trying to be nice all the time!"

What do you hope to do in the future?
"There are lots of exams I would like to take. I just want to keep on improving!"

Clare at work with her horse, Starlet.

Thanks to Rowanlea Riding School.

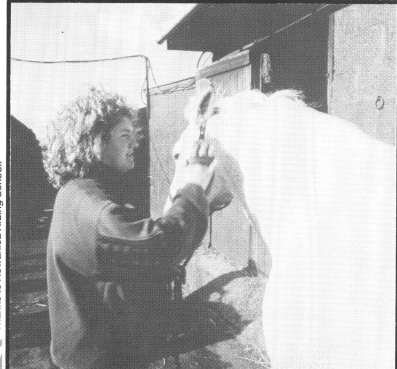

Everythin' you've ever wanted to know about bras, we've got it!

Under Cover!

◇ The bra has come a long way and no mistake! If you cast your mind back to the pictures in the history text books, only 100 years ago, women were stuffed, squashed and flattened into whalebone corsets and such creations, leaving a very uncomfortable and mis-shapen lady!

The first bra was claimed to be made by Warners in 1913, who were inspired by a rather fed up New York debutante who grabbed two hankies and got to work!

Mind you, it wasn't until 1935 that Warners realised that we all came in different sizes and invented the A, B, C and D cups! Despite that, even today, girls are *still* squashing themselves into the wrong size of bra, thinking they're a B-cup when they are in fact, a D-cup — ugly bumps, ahoy!

But enough of this lecturing, let's take a trip down memory lane with the brassiere . . .

★ ★ ★ ★

The 40's
During the Second World War, ladeez needed good, practical bras they could move in for everyday wear. Nowt fancy or frilly for these lasses! Berlei obliged by coming up with the Ultra-Lift and they *still* make it even now!

★ ★ ★ ★

The 60's
Flat, Twiggy-like chests were in, along with skinny, boyish bodies. Jean Shrimpton was the girl to look like! But later on, in the 60's, the once-popular bras were burned! Freedom for women meant freedom for every part of the bod, and at the 1968 Miss America contest, protesters threw bras, girdles and curlers into a Freedom trash can!

★ ★ ★ ★

The 70's
Freedom for chests was still the in thing. Girls ran to their nearest bra stockist to get themselves one of the new, light cotton support bras. They gave a smooth overall shape and paved the way for the body stocking as we know it today!

★ ★ ★ ★

The 80's
The natural, sporty shape became popular around then and sports bra sales increased 'cos women were becoming more athletic! The importance of exercise was stressed by doctors everywhere and women took to pounding the pavements along with Jane Fonda's workout! A soft, rounded shape was preferable for the ladeez of the 80's and the average size boob was 34B!

★ ★ ★ ★

The 50's
This is the period where chests were *big!* Curves were essential, à la Marilyn Monroe, and support and control was the order of the day!
Nylon was introduced into bras and after the war, girls could afford to buy the bras with the new style frills coming in every conceivable pastel shade — wow!

The 90's
Well, what can we say? In the 90's, anything goes! Whether you're small, large or medium, there's a bra to suit every shape 'n' size! The early 90's emphasised a good bit o' cleavage!

The average bra size is now 36C — a big jump from the 80's indeed, and it's a direct result of an overall better diet for the girls of today! Underwear ain't nothin' to be ashamed of and nowadays, it's worn as outerwear in the form of bustiers and corsets — look no further than Madonna!

BRA FACTS

☐ 75% of women wear bras that are too small.

☐ You could have your own bra made to measure for a stonking £185!

☐ Gossard's Wonderbra is very successful, and has sold over 10 million!

Choosing the right bra.

Small busts . . .
GIRLS who have small busts don't necessarily need underwiring, but if you want the appearance of a larger bust, Gossard's Wonderbra and Playtex Deep Plunge are the ones to go for. The best materials for your size are stretch-cotton, lycra and lacy numbers!

Medium busts . . .
BRAS with light underwiring and elastic support bands are suitable for medium−sized girls.

Large busts . . .
LARGER girls don't have to wear armour contraptions for support nowadays but a good underwired bra is essential. You *don't* need huge wide straps — many brands make large bras that are as pretty and as feminine as the smaller ones!

Underwear ladeez of yesteryear . . .
Marilyn Monroe
Jayne Mansfield
Brigitte Bardot
Jane Russell
Elizabeth Taylor
Sophia Loren

And todays counter parts!
Madonna (of course!)
Winona Ryder
Sherilyn Fenn
Dannii Minogue

And now for our tried and tested!

Tester: Tracey
Tried: Lillyets

"The straps on this were pretty thin, so they were very comfy and despite the soft material, it gave good support. The seams weren't visible even under a tight top. In fact, the only thing I wasn't keen on was the pinkish colour."

Marks: 9/10

Tester: Shona
Tried: White Gossard Underwired Bra

"This was a splendid fit. Because of my size (34 DD), it's difficult getting bras, so it's a joy to wear one made for my size! I loved the style, too!"

Marks: 10/10

Tester: Elspeth
Tried: Berlei 'Inspirations'

"This was nice — very 'uplifting' even without underwires! No scratching, no bits digging in, no nothing and a nice shape to boot!"

Marks: 9/10

Tester: Senga
Tried: BhS Black Strapless Bra

"This was comfy on — I didn't feel it was about to fall off as some strapless bras make you feel! I was impressed by the support considering it was strapless and it looked OK under clothes — gave a real impression of lift! Good for occasional wear as it was slightly scratchy."

Marks: 8/10

Tester: Jo
Tried: Cacharel Floral Underwired

"I liked the style of this and the material was lovely 'n' soft! It was a tiny bit wide at the back but otherwise it was great!"

Marks: 9/10

Tester: Felicity
Tried: Fiero by Berlei

"This was really comfy on! The straps didn't dig in at all and it gave good support even though it wasn't underwired. The style was nice but not lacy enough for me, I'm afraid! The only thing was, it tended to 'flatten' me!"

Marks: 7/10

Tester: Jan
Tried: White Gossard Wonderbra

"This was a perfect fit and it was really comfortable on. The material was quite soft, not scratchy at all, and the style was very pretty!"

Marks: 9/10

Tester: Pam
Tried: Berlei Sports Bra

"This was a bit constricting for everyday wear but v. comfy for sport. Support-wise, it's definitely cast iron — no probs! It didn't flatter the old curves as it tended to flatten, and for style, I like it, but only for sport!"

Marks: 9/10 (for support!)

Even best friends have their ups and downs. Three girls tell us their stories . . .

SARAH'S STORY

Claire had always been a bit of a tearaway but it wasn't until we got into secondary school that her wild streak really started to show. It was a mystery how we ever became friends in the first place. I was very quiet compared to Claire and preferred to stay in and read a book than go out and chase boys, which was how Claire spent most of her time. She was pretty as well whereas I was quite plain. I wasn't exactly jealous of her — it was more that I would have liked to have been more like her. When she was 15 she started fancying this guy in sixth year who was nearly 18. I'd never seen her quite so crazy about someone before and although I told her that he was quite a bit older than her and might want different things than she wanted, it didn't seem to stop her.

So, one night at a school disco, she asked him out. I couldn't believe it — I could never have done anything like that!

He said yes and she was over the moon. They arranged to go out the following weekend and she was in a real fluster about what she was going to wear and how she was going to do her hair. So we went shopping and bought her a really nice dress.

When I asked where they were going she looked a bit uncomfortable and said they'd decided on a restaurant and then the club in the high street. I knew as well as she did it was over 18 but as soon as I opened my mouth she glared at me and I knew I shouldn't say any more. Then she said she wanted to ask me a huge favour. She hadn't told her mum and dad what she was doing so was it OK if I covered for her? This was getting worse but I agreed to do it anyway.

immature

The following Saturday I was going to the pictures but Claire came round to my house to get changed so her mum wouldn't know what was going on.

By the time she was finished, Claire looked about 25, let alone 18!

We sneaked out of the house and we both went our separate ways. I still wasn't very happy with Claire, but what could I do?

Best Friend Blues

At about 10.30 p.m. me and my friends came out of the cinema and went along to the bus stop. We'd been waiting for about five minutes when I saw two figures walking towards us. As they got closer, I realised it was Claire and her boyfriend. Claire looked awful and soon I realised she was very drunk. According to Jamie they'd gone for a few drinks before their meal and then they'd had a bottle of wine in the restaurant and Claire obviously hadn't been able to handle it. I guessed she'd probably been trying to look older and more sophisticated but it hadn't worked!

I told Jamie I'd take her home with me and, hopefully, Mum would let her stay. If she went home in that state her mum would be furious.

Eventually, I managed to get her upstairs into my bed and I went to explain to Mum what had happened. She was pretty good about it and phoned Claire's mum to say that she was staying with us. She didn't mention what had happened because she said Claire had got herself into enough trouble and she didn't want to make things worse.

The next morning, Claire still felt terrible but she was really grateful for what I'd done to help her out. But I know she'd do exactly the same thing for me if I ever landed myself in trouble. After all, what are friends for?

NIKKI'S STORY

I was the first between me and my best friend, Amy, to have a boyfriend. I couldn't believe it. I'd fancied Matt for ages and finally one night at the school disco he asked me out.

Amy was really pleased for me because she'd known how I felt about Matt practically from the first moment I saw him. But she started to look a bit worried and I asked her what was wrong. She said that this was the first time either of us had been involved with a boy and what would happen to us?

I must admit I hadn't really thought about it before but I couldn't really see any problem. I would easily be able to split my time between them both, so neither of them would feel left out. It was nice to be so in demand!

The more I saw of Matt the more I liked him and he seemed pretty keen on me too. He was nice, really kind and considerate.

We were at a disco one night after we'd been going out together for a few months and I was really pleased to see Amy there with some friends from school. Actually, it was Matt who spotted her first but we both went over to talk to her and then me and Amy both went for a dance. Halfway through the record, Amy got a really weird look on her face and when I

asked her what was wrong she started to blush and shake her head. I decided there must have been some boy looking at her.

plans

The next week, I phoned Matt to ask him if he fancied going to the pictures that night. But he said he'd already made plans. I didn't mind, really, because I hadn't given him much notice.

The next day at school, Amy asked if I wanted to meet her on Saturday afternoon. I was seeing Matt in the evening but I'd have plenty of time to get ready to go out. So I met Amy in a café and she didn't look too happy. It took ages to get out of her what was bothering her but when I did I couldn't believe what I was hearing.

At the disco, Matt had been flirting like mad with Amy and that's why she had looked so strange. And every time I'd gone to get a drink or speak to someone Matt had been chatting her up.

Then on the Thursday, the night I had asked Matt to the pictures, he'd gone round to Amy's and asked her out saying he was going to finish with me soon, anyway. I was practically crying at this point but it was more with anger than anything else.

Amy had told him she wasn't interested and even if she had been I was her best friend and she could never even consider it.

I felt better after she'd told me that. At least I knew I wasn't about to lose my best friend even if I was going to have to dump the rat I'd been going out with for the past few months.

Amy sat really quietly for ages before asking if I was angry with her. I told her not to worry. We'd always be friends whatever happened — and how much worse could it get than this?

MARIA'S STORY

Joanna and I had known each other practically all our lives. We went to the same nursery school when we were very small and after that we'd gone on to primary school together. We hadn't always been in the same class but that hadn't stopped us from being the best of friends.

Everything we did, we did together. Of course, we had other friends too but none of them were quite as close as me and Joanna.

When we got into secondary school I started to notice a few little changes in our friendship. For a start, we had decided to take a lot of different classes so our timetables hardly ever coincided.

Lunchtimes were about the only free times we ever saw each other but we always made the most of them to catch up on all the gossip. In a way, it made things more interesting because we weren't spending all our time together but I couldn't help feeling things weren't the same as they used to be. Also, we both started to drift into different groups of girls. Hardly anyone hung around in just pairs probably because it was a lot more fun when you were with more than two or three people. But it meant that even outside school Joanna and I hardly ever saw each other anymore because we were starting to get involved in our own social lives.

tradition

Weekends were still quite good because we managed to keep up our tradition of going in to town and having a look round the shops and have a chat about everything that was going on at school. But even that wasn't to last for ever. One afternoon I was meeting Joanna as usual but when she turned up she wasn't on her own. With her was one of the girls she hung around with at school. I know I shouldn't have minded but I did. I felt that Joanna should have at least phoned me to let me know about the change of plan instead of just expecting me to go along with it. Then I thought I was being a bit silly. We both knew we had new friends now and maybe Joanna was just trying to introduce me to some of hers. Unfortunately, that wasn't how it turned out. We'd been in town for about an hour and I was starting to wonder what on earth I was doing there. Joanna and Meg were stuck together like glue, giggling and chattering away the same as we had done when we were younger. And there I was, tagging along at the back as if they hadn't even noticed I was there. Suddenly, I realised just how much things had changed and there was little point in trying to save my friendship with Joanna. For the past few years we had been living separate lives and because there had been so many other things happening we hadn't been making the effort to stick together. We probably thought we just would, whatever happened.

I felt sad that things hadn't worked out but I hoped that maybe one day we'd be friends again. I didn't really want to throw away all those years of friendship and I was pretty sure Joanna didn't want to either.

REPAIR

Fed up with your hair? Can't do a thing with it? We've got the answers to your hair problems!

Q. Help! It doesn't seem to matter how much conditioner I put on my hair, the ends are always dry and brittle. To make things worse it gets quite greasy at the roots. What can I do apart from getting it cut short?!

A. The longer your hair grows, the farther away the ends are from the scalp which is where the natural oils that keep your hair shiny and healthy are produced. That's why you need to use conditioner 'cos it takes the place of the natural oils. It's important to use the right conditioner for your hair too, as using the wrong one won't do you any good at all!

Using conditioner properly can make a big difference. You don't say exactly how long your hair is but if the ends are dry try massaging your conditioner into the ends then about a third to half way up the hair shaft. Leave it on for a minute or two then rinse thoroughly. Don't apply any conditioner to your roots as they don't need it and this will only make your hair extra greasy.

Q. My hair is naturally curly but I can't get it looking good. I have a chin-length bob but it looks a sight with a few curls here and wavy bits there. How can I get the life back into my curls?!

A. Lucky you having natural curls, although they can be a bit tricky at times!

If your hair is thick, a few layers might help because you'll lose some weight from your style which'll help the curls to spring back into action!

Apply some mousse, hair wax or even a little conditioner to the ends and try drying with your fingers for loads of twirly ringlets. If you don't have time for that invest in a diffuser-dryer that spreads the heat evenly and gently over your hair.

Q. I have a supposedly 'corkscrew curl' perm but it's a total nightmare! When it's just washed it looks great but by the end of the day or next morning it looks dry and frizzy and sticks out everywhere! Is there anything I can do with it?

A. Perms aren't easy to look after and you want the best from them you'll have to treat 'em with a bit of lurve and attention!

First of all, never brush permed hair 'cos it makes it frizz so use a wide-tooth comb to get rid of tangles.

Try to let it dry naturally as a hot hairdryer won't help matters. While your hair is still damp massage a dollop of hair wax into your curls. This should leave you with soft, glossy locks.

Try 'spritzing' with a spray of lukewarm water to dampen down frizzy bits.

Above all, remember to use a good conditioner for permed hair.

Q. I have very fine hair that's quite short just now but I'd really like to grow it. The trouble is that it's also completely straight. Should I get it layered?

A. Fine straight hair can be difficult but it also tends to be healthy and shiny.

It doesn't really look good very long unless it's thick, in which case, it looks fab but you won't go wrong with a chin/shoulder length style.

Stick to a simple bob, either with a fringe or without. Don't get it layered, whatever you do — fine straight hair looks better at one length 'cos it reflects the light making it look fuller.

Q. I've been trying to grow out my fringe but it's at the stage where I can't stand it any more — neither can my mum! The rest of my hair is quite long so it looks pretty bad — any suggestions?

A. You could try pulling your fringe up and back off your forehead, securing it with a clip or a few pins at the crown for neat style.

Or, you can ask your hairdresser to 'graduate' your hair down the sides so that it falls into a 'natural' curve, leaving you with most of the length and as it grows, get the length regularly trimmed so that eventually it'll all be one length!

Q. I do lots of sport, especially swimming so I have to wash my hair a lot, sometimes twice if I've been to the pool that day. It's really out of condition and I don't know what to do with it!

A. Start by choosing a style that's easy to look after. A short bob is a good alternative to cropped locks and doesn't take a lot of time to look after.

Choose a very mild shampoo for frequent use or a specially formulated brand for swimmers 'cos it's important to remove chlorine from your hair to prevent any damage. A light conditioner is probably a good idea, too. Apply it after washing, leave it for a minute or two then rinse really well.

This should work but if you've got time, try using a deep conditioning treatment once a week.

Wax/Oil

They add texture to short hair, shine to dry hair and gloss to curls, as well as smoothing down frizzy ends or bits that stick out!

Only use a tiny amount, though, or you'll end up with a not very attractive greasy style!

Q. My hair is really dull and boring and I'd like to brighten it up with some colour but I don't want to go for a permanent colour — Mum wouldn't let me, anyway! What should I use?

A. There are loads of semi-permanent and wash-in, wash-out colours to choose from.

Temporary rinses usually shampoo in then out after a couple of washes. They're great for adding a bit of life to your hair, making it nice 'n' shiny, too.

Semi-permanent colours can last for anything from 6-12 weeks and give a stronger colour. You can do it yourself with a shampoo-in variety or get your hairdresser to do it for you.

Try to stick to a colour that's in the same range as your natural colour — that way it'll still look right with your skin tone, eyes and eyebrows.

A subtle shade can simply add soft highlights to complement your colouring and looks better than a complete colour change.

But remember, check with Mum before you do anything!

Q. I'm sick of my greasy hair! I wash it every day and it looks OK for about an hour then it goes back to being greasy and horrible. What am I doing wrong?

A. You could well be using the wrong shampoo and technique! Greasy hair needs special attention and most shampoos for this type 'strip' the greasiness away, as well as the natural oils which keep your hair healthy and shiny. When this happens, your scalp produces even more natural sebum to make up for it which makes it greasy again!

Try out a very gentle shampoo that's pH balanced or go for a frequent-use brand.

Wet your hair through and work a small amount (about the size of a two pence piece) into the roots and through to the ends. Rinse well with loads of clean water then apply a blob of conditioner to the ends only and rinse again.

Q. I really hate going to the hairdresser! I'm too scared to say what I really want and I'm never happy with the results. I'd really like a perm but I'm terrified of what'll happen if it goes wrong!

A. Some 'trendy' salons can be intimidating but remember that you're the one that's handing over the cash so you're entitled to say what you want.

Try asking your friends where they go — if they're happy maybe you could give that salon a go.

When you go in to make an appointment, ask if they do consultations. If they do, arrange to see the stylist you'll be working with.

It's a good idea to take a few pictures of styles you like with you to give the stylist a better idea.

It might be best to 'try out' a salon before you go for a perm — you could go for a trim and see how you like it. Most salons do have someone that specialises in perms, though, so provided you're sure he/she knows what you want there shouldn't be any problems.

If you are unhappy with your hair after a visit to the salon, and if you explained what you wanted (i.e. an inch off the ends, not a short crop!) you are perfectly entitled to complain. Be pleasant about it, though, and you should get some sort of compensation — either a refund or they should agree to sort out your hair!

Try to be assertive and you should be OK!

Q. There are so many styling products around that I don't know what to use or what they do — I'm so confused!

A. There are always new products bouncing into the shops but there are a few basic ones that are easy to use once you know how and they can make quite a difference!

Mousse

It's great for adding volume and body to all styles and types of hair. Shake the can, squirt a golf-ball sized blob into your hand and work it into the roots then comb through the rest of your hair. Dry as normal.

Gel

Works well on short hair for extra 'life' at the roots. Don't use too much, though, and if you have dandruff go for an alcohol free brand that won't aggravate your scalp.

THE DATING GAME

Yeek! First date! What should you wear? What will you talk about? Don't panic! Check out our handy hints below, and you can't go wrong!

Where To Go

If he's a nice, considerate chappie who asks you where you'd like to go for your date, what should you reply?! If you're quite a chatty, outgoing sort of 'chick', then anywhere would do, really! But if you're shy, and cringe at the thought of having to keep the conversation going, then bowling or the cinema is the best plan. You can always talk about the film afterwards!

What To Wear

Obviously, on your very first date, yo want to look stunning and impress him! But before you start plastering on lippy and squeezing into that lycra mini — think!

Where are you going? If he's offered to take you bowling, or out for a pizza, you'll feel over-dressed and uncomfortable in the little sexy black number, no matter how fabsy it looked in the mirror before you came out. Settle for something you know you look good in, but which you also feel comfortable in. The whole night will be spoiled if you can't stop thinking about your skirt or you have to keep holding in your tummy!

Keep make-up to a minimum too. Just a touch is all you need to make you look great!

If you're going to a disco, though, you can go to town a bit! But don't get dressed up for the sake of it! Wear something that *you're* happy in. If that's the black lycra mini, then fine — if it's a floaty floral skirt, then stick with that!

If you don't actually know where you're going yet, you'll have to hedge your bets! Choose something that you would be able to wear if he takes you ice skating, but that wouldn't leave you feeling like a scruff if you go to the deesco!

But you'll know yourself what there is to do in your own town — if all there is is a cinema, chances are that's where you' be going!

What Will I Say?!!

First dates are always a bit awkward, whether you're quite friendly with the boy or not. You might get on easily with him in a crowd at school, but it's a bit different when it's just the two of you, and you're trying to eat pizza without getting cheese on your chin!

If you can arrange to go somewhere like bowling or skating, it'll be much easier to make conversation about what's going on.

If you're just going out for something to eat, chatting might be a bit harder, 'specially if you're both a teeny bit self-conscious. But don't panic!

DO talk about things you have in common, school, friends, etc.

DO ask him about himself and take an interest in what he says.

DO talk to him about films and music — everyone's interested in those!

O look him in the eye and smile a lot!

ON'T talk about your ex, how badly he eated you and how you're not really ver him yet.

ON'T pretend to be fascinated with ootball if you hate it.

ON'T chatter on for hours about people e doesn't know and couldn't care less bout!

ON'T bitch about his ex. Save that till ou know him better!

Money Money Money!

What about cash? We hear you cry. Vell, the best thing to do is take plenty 'ith you, and offer to pay your share. The nances are he won't let you — but just ffering will be a point in your favour! nd if he accepts, he was probably ondering how he would make his last ver stretch to two disco tickets and the us home!

I'll Call You . . ."

We've all heard this one before — aybe he will, and maybe he won't. But hatever happens, *do not* refuse to ave the house for a fortnight and set up amp by the phone. Even if he does call, e tension of three nights' staring at the hone willing it to ring will have spoiled ings a bit, and if he doesn't, you'll feel sed and demoralised.

Before you go out, ask your mum to ke a message if anyone calls, and to ay you'll call back. If he's keen, he won't ind waiting!

Steady Boyfriend

Woo! So the first date was a success, nd now you're 'going steady'! But ou're probably finding that it's not *quite*

the romantic set-up you thought!

At the beginning, spending time with him is by far the most important thing — much more important than homework, or mates, or walking the dog . . . However, it's not always wise to spend every waking moment together! How can he miss you if you never go away?! It just means you'll begin to take each other for granted much sooner than usual, and that would be a bit of a bummer!

Make time for your mates — even if you end up marrying him, you'll still need friends! When you're with them, try *not* to natter on about him *all* the time! Bo-ring!

There may come a time, though, when yer lad starts objecting to you seeing your mates or going out without him. Don't make the mistake of being flattered by this. Jealousy spells trouble, so let him know where he stands from the start — don't give in to "If you loved me you'd rather be with me" emotional blackmail.

But there are no hard and fast rules about how a relationship should be — as long as you're both happy, it's OK!

It's Over

Well, it happens to us all at one time or another, but it's still a pretty nasty thing to go through. Don't despair, though — we've compiled some do's and don'ts to help you out a bit!

If he finishes with you:

DON'T promise to change if you can try again. You can't become someone you're not.

DON'T rip up all the photos or cards you have which remind you of him. When you're over him, you'll only wish you hadn't!

DON'T haunt all the places you know he'll be. It'll be easier for you if you avoid him for a few weeks.

DO have a good cry.

DO have a girlie night out and enjoy it!

DO spoil yourself thoroughly for a few days!

If it hasn't worked out for you and you want to give him 'the chuck':

DON'T spend ages trying to justify yourself — just do it and go!

DON'T ask him whether his hunky pal is 'attached' or not at the moment.

DON'T give him a goodbye kiss.

DO tell him to his face. Messing about with notes and best mates is awkward and embarrassing.

DO stick to your guns. Make it clear from the start you want to finish, and you don't want to discuss anything.

DO give him back *all* his records or clothes which have been living in your bedroom. Then he won't have an excuse to turn up two days later.

'Clutching at straws' lines. Do not use, or fall for these!

1. I love you.
2. My mum'll be dead upset.
3. If you finish with me I'll kill myself/you/ your dog.
4. I can't live without you.
5. Let's just stay together until Karen's party.

'CHUCKING' thought for the day!

Look at this man. There are men like him in the world — what are you doing with your boyfriend?

Do not look at this girl. Do not remember that there are girls like her in the world. Do not wonder what your boyfriend is doing with you!

SURELY you're not serious?" I faced Craig, my eyes flashing little flecks of fire.

I could have cheerfully killed the love of my life at that moment.

"You said you'd come to town shopping with me this afternoon. You promised. You know I want something new for Donna's party."

"No Maxie. *You* said I'd go to town. I said I'd probably go to the match with the lads. It's the big game and they are expecting me."

Craig stood looking down at me, hands thrust into his jeans pockets, his handsome easy-going face set for once in firm hard lines.

I realised that today I wasn't going to get round him like I usually did, and I wasn't happy.

I'd been going out with Craig for three months and we had become an item. I wanted to spend all my time with him.

We had argued about this before. In fact we had argued a lot lately. Perhaps he was going off me. Well, there was only one way to find out.

apologise

"Right!" I yelled. "Go to the match if you want but if you do we're finished. I'll never, ever go out with you again."

"OK, Maxine, if that's what you want." Craig spoke quietly, and although his answer wasn't the one I wanted, or had expected to hear, I wasn't going to apologise or give in.

"Right," I said in turn. Then we just stood there like a couple of real fools until Craig muttered, "See you then," before he turned and walked away.

My stomach churned as I watched the back of his dark head. He couldn't be doing this. Just walking away from me like that. And putting a football match before our relationship. I could hardly believe it.

He was walking very slowly and I knew that I only had to call his name and he'd come hurrying back.

But even though I opened my mouth I couldn't do it. Blow him. Who did he think he was anyway? He wasn't the only guy in the world.

Let Craig go off with his mates and freeze at a football match. I

wasn't bothered in the slightest.

So why, I asked myself, did I feel like bursting into tears?

I decided to go to Donna's.

"What's up?" Donna asked looking at my stricken face when she opened her door, then she took me straight up to her room. "Have you and Craig been rowing again?"

"Yeah," I replied, the tremble in my voice giving the whole game away. "It's over for good this time."

"Well, I don't see why you're so bothered." Donna put a tape on as though this was just another normal visit, not the end of my world. "I mean he's not much to get upset about, is he? There are plenty of better looking boys around."

The cheek of it! I was about to say that compared to the guy she was seeing, Craig was gorgeous, but I thought better of it. I'd already lost one friend because of my big mouth and I didn't want to lose another.

A humble short story by Veronica Robinson

MATCH OF THE DAY

"Why do you like him so much anyway?" Donna asked.

And when I mumbled "I don't know," she tore a page from her homework book and drew a line down it, making two neat columns.

comparisons

"Right, this is what you do. You write the reasons for not liking him down one side and the reasons for liking him down the other. Then you draw comparisons. It's good, isn't it? I saw it in a magazine."

"Brilliant," I replied

sarcastically. But there was no stopping Donna. I took the pen she offered and began to write:

He prefers his mates to me, he calls me Babe, his hair is too short, his nose is too long. He thinks he looks like Mel Gibson (Well, he does a bit when he turns his head on one side) I scribbled a line through that one.

Donna peered over my shoulder and giggled.

"Not much going for him has he, poor guy. Now the reasons why you do like him. Come on, Maxie, get those feelings out."

I thought for a moment before making myself admit:

'Cos he's a hunk. He's kind, usually. He's my boyfriend and I love him.

flirting

Then all at once panic filled me. If I wasn't careful I'd lose him and it would be all my own fault for being so pig-headed.

He'd be off to the match in half an hour with all the guys and that

girl, Liz.

Liz is one of those girls who likes to pretend she's one of the boys, but that doesn't stop her flirting like mad with them.

I'd seen the way she'd eyed up Craig. She'd fancied him for ages. And if she ever got him I bet she would be too cute to try to completely change his life like I had tried to do.

Jumping to my feet I asked Donna if I could use her phone.

"Sure," she replied.

I charged down the stairs. "It doesn't take a minute to say that you're sorry."

It's easy too when the person you are apologising to is as understanding as Craig.

"Me too, Babe," he said, "but I really want to catch this game. See you tonight, eh?"

"Yeah," I answered hanging up my heart beating fast with relief as I shouted up to Donna to ask her if she wanted to go into town.

Illustration by Charmaine Peters

christian slater

★ ARE YOU A ★ S·T·A·R CHICK?

Are you a wild child or a wallflower? Find out which star *you're* most like!

★ ★ ★ ★ ★ ★ ★ ★ ★ ★ ★ ★ ★ ★ ★

1 How would you go about getting the lad o' your dreams?

Take a deep breath, march up to him and ask him out.

Be wherever *he* is and smile at him every chance you get — then wait for *him* to make the move!

Chat to him, dazzle him with your wit and personality and after you've got to know him, casually drop a hint about going out.

You'll wait for *him* to come to *you!*

Throw yourself at him as often as poss. so that he can't fail to get the message, then hope he asks you out!

2 There's an all-night party at your pal's house but your parents are a mite strict — how d'ya get round *this* one?

Construct a cunning 'I'm-staying-at-a-pal's-tonight' plan, with foolproof alibies, so that they'll *never* find out!

Tentatively ask them, stressing that you're mature and responsible, and hope for the best.

Ask them politely. If they say no, so what? You're still going whether they like it or not!

You won't go. You'll never be allowed even if you *do* ask.

Tell them you're going to a party, conveniently forgetting to mention it's an all night do'

3 Which type of music are you most into?

Mellow, George Michael, soul crooner-type stuff.

Hi Tec Dance music.

Rap and hip-hop.

Everything and anything, as long as it's gotta good melody.

Rock music.

4 Which one of these guys would be your ideal date?

A fun person like Vic Reeves — looks don't matter!

The swarthy, Italian type like Richard Grieco. Mmm . . .

The smart boy-next-door type like Jon New Kid . . .

A mean, tough dude like Johnny Depp.

A far-out, sexy dude like Michael Hutchence! Fwoarghh!

5 Where would you most like to go on a date?

For a coffee somewhere discreet. You'd hate it if your pals saw you and took the mickey!

To the funfair or cinema, where you're entertained from start to finish!

For a meal somewhere smart. You like to be treated well!

Down the bowling alley for some fun with the chums and then on to McDonalds!

For a walk somewhere romantic and quiet. You don't care much for crowded places.

6 Your best pal runs off with the boy you've fancied for ages. What do you do?

Laugh it off. You win some, you lose some!

Start a hate campaign and spread rumours about her to get her back for doing the dirty.

Threaten to floor her, then decide she just ain't worth your time!

You don't speak to her for days until she apologises.

Pretend it never happened.

7 Out of this lot, how would you most like to be dressed?

Casual, denim jackets, jeans, raggy T-shirts and most things black. You don't care too much.

Plain, neat clothes.

Smart but trendy suits, bright colours — fairly up to the minute stuff.

Clubby gear, skin-tight, eye-catching and figure-flattering!

Absolutely anything that'll get you noticed and 'wowed' at — it doesn't matter how stupid it looks!

8 What do you do to reee-lax?!

Go out raving at a local nite spot!

Curl up with a book and some coffee. Who needs a wild night?

Spend an evening of total self-indulgence with a bath, manicure, hot oil treatments and some long, girlie phone calls!

Get a pal round for a chat and some videos.

Go to the cinema with some pals if there's something good on!

9 If you had £1000, what would you be most likely to spend it on?

- You'd invest it in shares or stick it all in the bank to save for a rainy day.

- Probably on some good cause — a charity, like helping to save the rainforests.

- Your family. You'd buy them some nice things they've always wanted and treat yourself, too!

- Having a good time! You'd treat your pals to a slap-up weekend and go crazeeee!!

- Yourself! You'd go mad in your fave clothes shop and buy all the expensive stuff you couldn't normally afford.

0 In the attractiveness stakes, how do you see yourself?

- Purritty darned gorgeous!

- You're not great-looking, but you always make an effort and dress to suit yourself.

- You suppose you look OK but you don't worry too much about stuff like that.

- Quite attractive and nice-looking, but your personality's much better!

- Nothing special. Average and non-descript.

1 Outta this lot, what would you never do?

- Talk or bitch about your closest pal.

- Take the blame for a friend in any situation!

- Steal another girl's boyfriend.

- Lie to a friend.

- Admit to bitching/telling tales about someone.

2 What comes closest to your ambition?

- To skydive from a B52 before you're 25!

- To earn as much money as possible and be your own boss!

- To have a little car and house, a family and a stress-free job — you hate competitiveness.

- To be happy in whatever you decide to do.

- To be totally successful in your job and get to the top of the career ladder — a corporate executive, maybe!

CONCLUSIONS

Colour circled	Score
Green	1
Blue	2
Orange	3
Yellow	4
Pink	5

12-19

You are a little miss Janet Jackson indeed! You want an easy time, everyone to like you and all the good things in life! There ain't a nasty bone in your body but it doesn't make you a doormat, no siree! You probably get away with murder, but beneath that timid facade, you're tons of fun and make a great, loyal pal!

20-27

You're just like Winona, lover of Johnny and an all-round nice gal! You mind your own business and let people get on with theirs, with no pretensions about yourself — people can take you as you are or get stuffed. You're not aggressive and avoid fights at all costs, but you're no chicken — you're a tough cookie underneath and stand up for your rights!

28-35

You could be Kylie Minogue! 'Fun' is your favourite word — and even better if everyone else joins in! You haven't got time to worry about school marks, boys or parents, and you make an effort to get on well with everyone, 'cos friends are important, right? You never let anything get you down and shrug off things most people would be in tears over, but you haven't got time for that — you've got to party, party, paartaaay!

36-43

Well, no-one gets on your wrong side, Ms Cathy Dennis! You know what you want and go for it, no punches pulled! You're a loyal friend and keep your fave people around you at all times to brighten you up when you're feeling down. You can be a very determined young lady, but fair-minded at the same time, demanding respect from all 'n' sundry. However, you ain't averse to a wild time on occasion — you know how to have a good time, an' no mistake!

44-50

Hold it, hold it! You're acting like the entire world's against you! Aggressive, bitchy, domineering . . . you're a dead ringer for Madonna in the personality stakes! You want everything — now! You can't stand it when someone upstages you and do what you can to get revenge. Your favourite pastime is yourself, whether it's pampering, talking about, laughing at, whatever. You know how to treat yourself well, but not other people! You can't be all bad, though, 'cos everyone wants to be your pal! All the gossip happens around you, y'see, and you know it only too well!

AUTUMN

HARVEST TIME

Fall under the spell of autumn's warmest colours.

Left vertical text: "Jumper and hat from Top Shop." and "Leggings from Snob."

HARVESTY HUES

Rusts, coppers, browns, creams, golds — all colours that make you think of autumn leaves. These colours look brilliant at this time of year and bring out the best in most skin tones.

MAKE-UP

Now's the time of year to experiment with the rich colours you can see all around. However, bear in mind that you should only accentuate your eyes or your lips — accentuate both and it won't do you any favours.

BASE — A smooth creamy matt base is the order of the day so pick a suitable foundation (why not try a compact foundation?). A thorough puffing of powder will keep things where they should be!

EYES — Go on, be wild 'n' free! Using just a little can have quite a 'stunning' effect. Here we used an amber shadow all over the lower lid. Then using a cocoa brown and a small flat brush, a little of the colour was taken along the lower and upper lashes then along the outer socket. A light stroking of brown-black mascara finished off the eyes.

LIPS — We used a spicy ginger moisturising lipstick which again we applied using a brush. Pimps!

AUTUMN TIPS

● Now's the time to enhance your natural hair colour with a warm autumn tone. Use a temporary colour, wash in, leave for around 30 mins, then rinse out. Depending on the brand it should last for 4-6 washes.

● With the chillier winds a-blowin', it's a good idea to make sure you step up the moisturising part of your skin care routine. You may need a creamier moisturiser over the colder months, as your skin's more prone to dryness then.

● You don't have to go out and buy a whole new autumn wardrobe. First wear lots of layers! Team polo-necks with leggings, mini skirts and shirts for a cosy look.

● Autumn's the time to invest in a hat — and wear it!

● If you're feeling the chills — wear a couple of pairs of cotton-mix tights. The effect's like thermal 'loons'!

● Look deep into your eyes and check out any teeny specks of colour in the iris. Use eyeshadows in these tones to bring out the warmth of your colouring.

● Don't let the prospect of the wintry months to come turn you into a couch potato. Join an aerobics class, play squash, go swimming or weight training — just do anything to work off those extra calories we all eat come the big chill.

◄ Boots from Shellys. ►

ME!

We've got all you need to know to keep up with the Green Scene.

GO FOR

Phew, all this talk about being green and environmentally friendly can fair give yer a bit of a turn! When it comes down to what you really need to know, all the squillions of facts 'n' figures floating around can make things a mite confusing . . . We've got together the important points 'n' facts about keeping the environment a rather fetching shade of green!

A Load Of Rubbish

OK, so none of us really wants to spend much time considering what goes on in the recesses of our bins . . . but there's a whole lot more to rubbish than meets the eye!

■ At the moment, about 30% of paper products we buy are made from recycled paper. When you consider that over 130 million trees are cut down simply to provide us with wood 'n' paper — we could do with a whole lot more being recycled!

■ It actually takes 40% less energy to make paper from recycled fibre than to make it from new pulp.

■ In Britain, about six billion glass bottles and jars are used every year . . . phew! But, glass can actually be recycled for ever more! All that's needed are bottle banks to keep the glass recycling biz going and they actually turn over a profit . . . so we save heaps of money as well.

■ Every year we go through 10 billion tins and cans and it makes up 10% of the rubbish in our bins. About five billion of this figure is made up of drink cans . . . Seemingly placed end to end, the line of them would reach the moon. That's some amount of cans!

■ The good news is, recycling aluminium cans saves 95% of the energy it would take to make a new one and it cuts down pollution by exactly the same amount. Yippee!

If you think about it . . . all the rubbish that we throw away has to go somewhere . . . and it's obvious that if we don't cut down on rubbish and increase the quantity of recyclable waste . . . we're fast gonna run out of space for dumping — never mind considering the adverse effects all the pollution will have on the land.

The Beauty Biz

Now, just because you want to go green and cruelty-free doesn't mean you have to let standards drop and give up looking good . . . There's always an alternative . . .

■ *Previously, make-up and other beauty products were pretty bad offenders when it came to animal testing and 'strange' additives . . . but now there are heaps of brands which are completely cruelty free 'n' easy! Have a look around your local chemist or department store and see which brands are cruelty-free — you'll be amazed at the choice. If it doesn't actually say on the packaging . . . ask someone behind the counter to check for you.*

■ *Back to the old aerosol story again! If you are still using cans of hairspray, anti-perspirant and suchlike which contain CFC's (nasty gases which tear up the protective ozone layer) . . . then wise up! Isn't it about time you switched to the pump action variety?*

■ *When it comes down to packaging although we want our lotions 'n' potions to look nice, plump for simply-packed products . . . that'll save on resources. Also, look out for companies that use recyclable and/ or biodegradable packaging or even ones that have a refill option! Fabsy, eh!*

GRE

The Wild Side

What's happening in the world isn't just affecting us . . . so here's what's going on out in the wilds . . .

■ Something like 40% of Britain's 'heaths' have been destroyed and just over a third has been lost since the end of WW2. Nearly 200 square kilometres has been made into motorway!

■ As many as half the world's species live in the forests of the world . . . and an area equal to about 20 football pitches of forest is destroyed every minute.

■ Forests and such areas are vital to the survival of every animal, because due to all that photosynthesis stuff, vegetation and plantlife absorb carbon-dioxide and leave lovely sweet oxygen for us to breathe . . . so basically we can't afford to lose any more!

■ Much plantlife and livestock is being destroyed and polluted by acid rain. All the nasty gases and chemicals expelled from factories are carried thousands of miles on the wind and moisture in the atmosphere so obviously when it rains . . . down comes chemicals 'n' all!

So, it can all seem quite depressing and hopeless . . . but not so — there's heaps you can do to help!

■ Easy one first. Don't litter. Keep your immediate environment tidy and most of all, clean!

■ Sort out your rubbish before the bin men come to collect it. Take all bottles to the bottle dump and aluminium can skips. If there aren't any in your area maybe you could see about campaigning to get them.

■ Choose cruelty-free products with the minimum of packaging and don't use aerosols. Need we say why?

■ Try to buy recycled paper products when you can . . . like writing paper, kitchen and loo rolls, cards and wrapping paper . . . every little bit helps.

■ Try to re-use plastic bags for as long as possible . . . or opt for using paper ones instead — recycled of course!

■ Try to keep your lifestyle as clean and healthy as possible . . . this'll mean less use and abuse of our environment.

■ If you feel strong about any particular 'Green' issues . . . get involved! Nip down to the library for information and addresses of organisations you might want to join.

Room Wit

Old Fashioned Girl!

● Ask your mum/granny etc. for any empty perfume bottles or look for old fashioned jars and tins in second hand shops. Arrange them in a group for extra effect.

● Dried flowers look a treat in a wicker basket or china vase placed on your desk or dressing table.

● Cover an old table with a crisp, white tablecloth or other material for an instant dressing table. Add a wooden framed mirror for an old fashioned 'cottagey' look!

● Have a rummage through the old family albums for a few old black and white snaps. Stick them in simple wooden frames. Or try doing the same with your fave poster then get some smaller, postcard-sized prints and group them all together for extra effect.

● Swap a high-tec radio/alarm for a traditional 'bell' alarm clock that no-one can sleep through of a morning!

● Old linen hankies or napkins look good in a little wicker basket filled with pot-pourri.

● Try buying or making some stencils, then arm yourself with a few paint testers and brush some colour onto your walls, door, round the window, on an old plain wooden chair — the possibilities are endless! (It might be an idea to ask Mum first though . . .)

● Wooden boxes, brass picture frames and plain china or glass containers look good without being fussy. Keep well clear of frills and loads of floral print curtains or duvet covers and try to avoid too much pink or peach. Go for simple cream and white with a few hints of colour instead!

● Cover up an old chair with a piece of pure white material, or if you're feeling more adventurous go for a bold, geometric print in black/white or bright colours.

● Use cheap plastic frames or frameless clip frames to frame black and white postcards. Stick them on white card first for a dramatic effect. Put them in small groups rather than simply all over the walls.

● For instant glamour fill a glass or perspex box with junk jewellery.

● Try your hand at sewing and make some cushion covers in dramatic black and white checks or for a really bold effect try silver lamé or satin!

● Use plain or bold coloured ceramic vases or jars to hold make-up brushes, cotton wool balls or as a handy pencil holder.

● Matt black plastic or china trays are great for holding all your bits 'n' pieces.

● Plain white or very pale walls look great with bold black and white. Go for chrome accessories like a bedside lamp with a simple grey duvet cover. Or use a couple of bright colours like yellow, green or red!

h A View!

Cheap 'n' cheerful ideas to help you give your bedroom the makeover treatment!

BEFORE YOU BEGIN . . .

Your bedroom is your own space where you go for a bit of privacy from the rest of your family! Whether it's to catch up on some homework, listen to your own music or have a gossip with your mates, you know you can relax! It's probably the only place in the house where you can have some say on 'decor', too! 'Course, that doesn't mean your parents are going to hand over stashes of cash for you to buy a whole lot of new furniture and paint, no siree! That means you'll have to make the most of what you've already got instead!

GET STARTED!

Discuss what you'd like to do with your mum but be reasonable — not many parents go for black/purple walls! If you do want to paint the walls, door etc., offer to do it yourself or enlist a few willing chums to give you a hand.

Go for a colour that's easy to live with. Pale colours make a small room look bigger so go for subtle shades if you want a lighter, roomier effect.

You don't have to go for major redecorating, though, especially if you like the colour your bedroom is already. Try choosing another one that'll complement it instead, so that whatever else you buy or make it'll blend in.

Now's the time to start scrounging! Ask your mum/granny/auntie if they have any old bits of material or curtains. If they're big enough you can use them to hide an ugly chest of drawers or chair by just throwing them over. Take a trip round local second hand shops, flea markets and car boot sales. Have a good rake around and you're bound to come across a few fab bargains! And don't chuck something out just because the colour isn't right. A lick of paint soon transforms just about anything!

High-Tec Mizz!

LESSON IN LOVE

THAT'S IT. I'VE FAILED. THERE WASN'T ONE QUESTION I KNEW IN THE ENTIRE TEST.

YEAH, I KNOW. WHO KNOWS ANYTHING ABOUT THE WEIMAR REPUBLIC ANYWAY?

I BET EVERYONE'S FAILED. THERE'S NO WAY ANYONE COULD HAVE PASSED IT.

THERE'S COLIN. I BET HE'S PASSED IT.

YEAH, WELL, YOU KNOW WHAT HE'S LIKE. HE ALWAYS PASSES EVERYTHING. HE'S A TOTAL SWOT.

COME ON, IT'S NOT HIS FAULT IF HE'S GOOD AT HISTORY, IS IT? WHAT DO YOU EXPECT HIM TO DO, GET IT WRONG CN PURPOSE?

WHAT ARE YOU STICKING UP FOR HIM FOR? HE'S A TOTAL WALLY!

YEAH, KAREN'S RIGHT, JILL. DO YOU FANCY HIM OR SOMETHING?

OF COURSE I DON'T! LOOK, I WANT TO GO TO THE SHOPS ON THE WAY HOME. I'LL SEE YOU LATER.

THEY'RE REALLY HORRIBLE TO COLIN. I DON'T KNOW WHY THEY CAN'T JUST LEAVE HIM ALONE. IT'S NOT AS IF HE'S DONE ANYTHING TO THEM.

THEN . . .

HI, JILL. LISTEN, I'M REALLY GLAD I'VE MET YOU. I TRIED TO CATCH YOU AFTER SCHOOL BUT I MISSED YOU.

OH, HI, COLIN. WHAT DO YOU WANT?

YOU KNOW I'M EDITING THE SCHOOL MAG THIS YEAR? I THOUGHT YOU MIGHT BE ABLE TO HELP WITH THE ARTWORK. I ASKED MR BURNS IN THE ART DEPARTMENT AND HE SAID YOU WERE REALLY GOOD AT CARTOONS.

ANYTHING! WE'RE REALLY SHORT OF MATERIAL. YOU KNOW, CARICATURES OF THE TEACHERS. ANYTHING LIKE THAT.

I DON'T KNOW . . . WHAT SORT OF STUFF DO YOU WANT?

WELL . . . I'M NOT SURE. LOOK, I'LL LET YOU KNOW, OK?

THE NEXT MORNING . . .

OK, JILL, WHAT'S THIS ABOUT YOU AND COLIN?

WHAT ARE YOU TALKING ABOUT?

COME ON, THE SECRET'S OUT! MONICA SAW YOU WITH COLIN LAST NIGHT! SO THAT WAS WHERE YOU WERE SNEAKING OFF TO!

COME ON, YOU DON'T REALLY THINK THERE'S ANYTHING GOING ON, DO YOU? I RAN INTO HIM AND HE ASKED ME TO DO SOME STUFF FOR THE SCHOOL MAGAZINE, THAT'S ALL.

SO ARE YOU GOING TO DO IT OR WHAT?

YEAH, WHY NOT? IT SHOULD BE A LAUGH.

SO . . .

HI, COLIN, I'VE BROUGHT SOME STUFF FOR THE MAGAZINE IF YOU WANT IT.

GREAT! LET'S HAVE A LOOK, THEN.

THERE'RE A FEW CARTOONS OF TEACHERS — J.R., MRS MUNRO, TEXY AND PEOPLE LIKE THAT — AND A COUPLE OF CARTOON STRIPS. ARE THEY ANY USE?

THEY'RE BRILLIANT! YOU'RE REALLY GOOD, YOU KNOW THAT? LISTEN, IS THERE ANY CHANCE YOU COULD DO A COUPLE OF ILLUSTRATIONS FOR A STORY ONE OF THE THIRD YEARS HAS WRITTEN?

OK. WHEN DO YOU NEED IT?

AS SOON AS POSSIBLE. WE'RE WAY BEHIND ALL THE DEADLINES ALREADY.

OK. I'LL DO IT OVER THE WEEKEND.

AT THE WEEKEND . . .

OH, THERE'S THE DOORBELL — WONDER WHO IT IS . . .

OH, HI, COLIN, IT'S YOU. WHAT DO YOU WANT?

HI, JILL. SORRY TO BOTHER YOU AT THE WEEKEND, BUT I'VE GOT SOMETHING THAT NEEDS ILLUSTRATED REALLY URGENTLY. CAN YOU DO IT?

YEAH, OK. DO YOU WANT TO COME IN?

WELL, WHAT DO YOU THINK?

YEAH, IT SHOULD BE FINE. I CAN DO A BIG DRAWING FOR THE START THEN A COUPLE OF SMALLER CARTOONS TO GO WITH IT.

BRILLIANT! LISTEN, THERE WAS SOMETHING ELSE I WANTED TO ASK YOU AS WELL . . .

WHAT?

WELL . . . I WAS WONDERING IF MAYBE YOU MIGHT WANT TO GO OUT SOMETIME — TO THE PICTURES OR SOMETHING . . .

I DON'T KNOW . . . MAYBE . . . I'M NOT SURE. I'LL LET YOU KNOW, ALL RIGHT?

OK. LOOK, I'D BETTER GO. I'LL SEE YOU ON MONDAY, OK?

WHAT AM I GOING TO DO? I'M BEGINNING TO REALLY LIKE COLIN BUT I'LL GET SLAGGED ROTTEN FROM JO AND KAREN IF I GO OUT WITH HIM . . . MAYBE I COULD SEE HIM AND NOT TELL ANYONE . . .

SO . . .

COLIN? IT'S ME. LISTEN, DO YOU STILL WANT TO GO OUT SOMETIME?

OK, THEN. WHAT ABOUT MONDAY NIGHT?

YEAH, OF COURSE. WHY?

. . . GREAT. I'LL COME ROUND FOR YOU ABOUT HALF-SEVEN, OK?

ON MONDAY . . .

HEY, JILL, DO YOU FANCY GOING SKATING TONIGHT? THAT NEW RINK'S OPEN NOW.

NO, I CAN'T . . . I'VE GOT SOME STUFF TO DO FOR THE SCHOOL MAG . . .

WHAT, AGAIN? YOU'RE GETTING AS BAD AS THAT SWOT COLIN!

THIS IS TERRIBLE! IF THEY KNEW I WAS GOING OUT WITH COLIN, I'D NEVER HEAR THE END OF IT . . .

THAT NIGHT . . .

THANKS FOR WALKING ME HOME, COLIN. I HAD A REALLY NICE TIME.

ME TOO. DO YOU WANT TO DO IT AGAIN SOMETIME?

YES, THAT'D BE NICE.

THE NEXT MORNING . . .

WHERE WERE YOU LAST NIGHT, JILL? I TRIED TO PHONE YOU BUT YOUR MUM SAID YOU'D GONE OUT.

OH, YEAH . . . I . . . I WENT OUT FOR A RUN.

WHAT ABOUT THOSE DRAWINGS YOU SAID YOU HAD TO DO?

OH . . . I FINISHED THEM EARLIER THAN I THOUGHT.

THE NEXT EVENING . . .

SO WHAT TIME DOES THE FILM START?

QUARTER TO. IT'S SUPPOSED TO BE REALLY GOOD. PHIL AND PETE SAW IT LAST NIGHT.

OH, NO, THERE'S JO AND KAREN! LET'S SLOW DOWN!

WHY? WHAT'S THE PROBLEM?

NOTHING . . . IT'S JUST THAT I TOLD THEM I WAS STAYING IN TONIGHT.

SO WHAT? TELL THEM YOU CHANGED YOUR MIND.

I JUST DON'T WANT THEM TO SEE US, THAT'S ALL.

OH, I GET IT. YOU DON'T MIND GOING OUT WITH ME BUT YOU DON'T WANT ANYONE TO KNOW ABOUT IT, IS THAT IT?

IT'S NOT THAT, IT'S JUST . . .

DON'T BOTHER TRYING TO EXPLAIN. LET'S JUST FORGET IT, OK? I'M GOING HOME. YOU'RE JUST AS BAD AS THEY ARE, YOU KNOW THAT?

I CAN'T BLAME HIM FOR BEING ANNOYED. HOW COULD I BE SO STUPID? I REALLY LIKE HIM AND IF JO AND KAREN OR ANYONE ELSE CAN'T ACCEPT IT, WELL, I DON'T NEED THEM AS FRIENDS . . . THE PROBLEM IS, WHAT AM I GOING TO DO NOW?

THE NEXT MORNING . . .

HI, COLIN. LISTEN, I WANTED TO TALK TO YOU. I'M REALLY SORRY ABOUT LAST NIGHT AND I WAS WONDERING IF YOU'D LIKE TO GO OUT SOMEWHERE?

YEAH? LIKE WHERE — BEHIND A BUS SHELTER SO NO-ONE WILL SEE YOU?

NO . . . LOOK, I WANTED TO ASK YOU IF YOU WERE DOING ANYTHING ON SATURDAY.

NO, WHY?

WELL, JO'S HAVING A PARTY. I THOUGHT YOU MIGHT LIKE TO COME WITH ME.

TO JO'S PARTY? IF WE GO TOGETHER THE WHOLE SCHOOL WILL KNOW ABOUT IT. EVERYONE'S GOING.

I KNOW. NOW DO YOU WANT TO GO OR NOT?

HMM . . . I THINK I COULD FORCE MYSELF . . .

THE END

"I WANT TO LOOK OLDER!"

"Help!" Claire screamed. "I badly need a make-over! I've always looked much younger than all of my friends and I reckon it's time for a change! Can you help?" We certainly did, take a look for yourselves . . .

"I really like this big jumper . . . the colours are great! And, for the first time ever, I actually suit leggings!!"

Black leggings from Tammy Girl, jumper from Top Shop.

FACTFILE

NAME: Claire Brown
LIVES: Blackheath
AGE: 11
HOBBIES: Dancing and swimming.
FAVE FILM: 'Home Alone'
FAVE POP STAR: Kylie
FAVE FILM STAR: Macaulay Culkin

Well, Claire, were you chuffed with your new look?!

"Yes, I really like it! I've always looked much younger than all of my friends, but not now! I can't believe how much older I look! I'm so small that a lot of clothes don't suit me."

"Yeah, this look's different, I'd never ever be daring enough to wear those leggings, but I like them!"

Denim jacket, polo neck jumper and floral leggings, all from Tammy Girl.

"Now this is my favourite, definitely. I love the top with the frilly sleeves!"

White top from Empire. Black and red stripe waistcoat and trousers, from Tammy Girl.

Shots: Sarah Hutchings
Hair and make-up: Liz Pugh

family

**All these folks are rich, recognised — and related!
We check out the most famous showbiz families . . .**

BROTHERLY LOVE!

■ **Matt and Kevin Dillon** — they may have their parents in common but we reckon Matt Dillon stole more than his fair share of the family good looks. Sorry , Kev!

■ **Jon 'n' Jordan Knight** — how different can two bruvs be — Jordan the singing star who loves being in the spotlight, and Jon the shy, retiring type. One thing they share is the size of their bank balance!

■ **Donnie and Mark Wahlberg** — Donnie may be by far the richer of the Wahlberg brothers, but we reckon he'd rather be a ruff-tuff rapper like Mark!

■ **William and Alec Baldwin** — judging by our pic they share the same clothes too! Surely rich movie stars can afford at least one bow tie, as well as a razor!

■ **Jon, Tim and Andrew Farriss** — these brothers make up the backbone of INXS but they're constantly upstaged by "that geezer wot went out with Charlene from 'Neighbours'." Never mind lads, we love you!

TOP SCREEN MUMS!

■ **Madge Bishop** (née Mitchell, then Ramsay!) — anyone who's managed to survive after bringing up two monsters like Charlene (Kylie Minogue) and Henry (Craig McLachlan) deserves to win an award! She's even had to 'mother' dopey Harold!

■ **Dianne Wiest** — this movie lass has appeared in three major films as a mom to some young geezers — Corey Haim

and Jason Patric in 'The Lost Boys', Martha Plimpton and Leaf Phoenix in 'Parenthood', not forgetting Winona Ryder in 'Edward Scissorhands' — she even fostered the jaggy-fingered one in that movie for a while! She's had her fair share of bother from each of them, the poor girl!

■ **Michelle Fowler** — the mother of soap's brat Princess, the one and only Vicky, and she's also Walford's most glamorous single parent!

ACTING FOLKS!

■ **The Sheens** — Now here's a family — Pop Martin started off the acting tradition appearing in movies such as 'Apocalypse Now' and 'Wall Street', but his two sons sure have followed in his footsteps! Charlie Sheen and Emilio Estevez first started acting at school with two other sets of famous brothers — Sean and Christopher Penn and Rob 'n' Chad Lowe. Since then they've appeared in many a fab movie and twice starred together, in 'Young Guns' and 'Men At Work'. Not to be outdone, sister Renee Estevez has got in on the act, appearing in 'Heathers' amongst other things!

■ **The Donovans** — First Jason starred as Scott Robinson in 'Neighbours', quickly becoming the top soap star of the moment, and now his crumbly dad's taking over as the Donovan soap chap! Terence appeared in 'Home and Away' then he moved to Melbourne to meet some new 'Neighbours'!

■ **The Fondas** — the Fonda acting dynasty started off with Oscar-winning grandad Henry, continued with hippies Peter and Jane in the Sixties, and are now bang up to date with Bridget!

MUSICAL FAMILIES!

■ **The Osmonds** — in the Seventies Donny, Marie and li'l Jimmy were the squeaky clean rulers of pop, and sported the worst fashions of all time! Their nephews The Osmond Boys hope to repeat the success in the Nineties, but unfortunately the family fashions haven't improved as you can see.

affair!

SISTERS!

Gillian and Gayle Blakeney — they play sisters Caroline and Christina Alessi on 'Neighbours', and sometimes Gayle's snogging partner Stefan Dennis even has trouble telling the twins apart!

■ **Rosanna and Patricia Arquette** — these acting sisters both share the habit of going out with weird pop stars — Rosanna used to snog Peter Gabriel and the lead singer of The Blue Nile, while Patty used to live with someone from the Red Hot Chilli Peppers!

■ **Kylie and Dannii Minogue** — they've both been in Aussie soaps, they churn out hit singles by the dozen, they've appeared in flop movies and they fancy Lenny Kravitz — but that's where the similarities end!

Five Star — the Pearson brothers and sisters blitzed the charts in the early Eighties with their sequinned jumpsuits and extravagantly choreographed dance routines, but hit the headlines for the wrong reasons when Lorraine was chucked by Eddie Murphy and they all lost their money!

The Jacksons — these Seventies soul superstars had hits a-plenty and their own TV and cartoon series, and then offspring Michael and Janet went on to get even richer! Unfortunately the richer they got, the weirder they all turned!

FAMILY TIES!

■ **Spike Lee** certainly believes in keeping it in the family — his sister, Joie, has appeared in most of his movies, his father, Bill, usually writes the music for them and his brother is the official photographer!

■ **Leaf Phoenix** starred in 'Parenthood' as Martha Plimpton's brother — Martha was going out with Leaf's real-life brother, River, at the time!

■ **When Sly Stallone** was looking for someone to star as his son in 'Rocky V' he had to search no further than his own doorstep — his real lad, Sage, got the part!

■ **Wilson Phillips** are made up of three offspring from Sixties supergroups The Beach Boys and The Mamas And The Papas — unfortunately, Carnie and Wendy Wilson's dad, Brian, is a bit of a nutter!

■ **Sean Connery and Roger Moore,** the two best Bonds, both have kids who've appeared on telly, too. Rog's daughter is the woman decked out in black in the Scottish Widows TV ads, and Jason Connery was recently seen starring in 'The Secret Life Of Ian Fleming', as the creator of James Bond! Another spook family coincidence — Jason's best known for starring as a rather merry man in 'Robin Of Sherwood', and one of his da's latest films was, yes!, 'Robin Hood: Prince Of Thieves'!

Sensible

Eat your way to a healthier diet with our guide to good food!

GETTING STARTED!

How you start the day can make a big difference. Always have something to eat even if you just grab a slice of toast and a glass of fresh orange juice.

If you think about it, you won't have eaten since teatime the night before so if you skip breakfast your blood sugar level will be down, leaving you without any energy to start the day!

'Course, that doesn't mean you should stuff your face with heaps of sugary cereals or chocolate bars in the morning!

Try a bowl of tasty muesli or cereal with bran (for extra fibre) and use skimmed milk instead of the full fat, creamy variety to keep the calories down.

Or go for a couple of slices of wholemeal toast with a thin layer of butter or low-fat spread.

Try herbal tea or a glass of sparkling mineral water with a slice of lemon — a very refreshing way to start the day!

FOOD FACTS

The more you know about what you're eating, the easier it is to eat the right food for a healthy diet!

The secret behind healthy eating

Scoffing!

to fill your face with as much of
e good stuff as you like, but keep
way from the 'baddies' wherever
ossible. It doesn't take a genius to
ork out that a diet of crisps,
hocolate, burgers and chips isn't
oing to do much good, so go for
esh fruit, wholemeal bread and diet
ft drinks etc. when you can.

There are basically five
ategories of food and you should
at a certain amount each day.

RUIT 'N' FIBRE!

Fresh fruit is one of the best
ods you can eat — and it's totally
atural! It's packed with natural
ugar, vitamins, minerals and
ssential fibre and it's tasty too! You
hould eat at least one piece of fruit
day but try to eat more. The
esher the better so buy a little bit
hen you want and that way you'll
et all the 'goodness' from it!

Fibre is very important 'cos it
eeps your digestive system
orking properly. You'll find heaps
f fibre in natural, unprocessed food
at has no (or very few) additives
ke wholemeal bread and pasta,
atural brown rice, lentils and other
ulses, fruit and veg including
otatoes. Obviously, you can't
unch a chunk of orange peel but
y not to peel the skin from apples,
ears, peaches or grapes as they're
l great sources of protein.
emember to give them a good
ash first, though!

Cereals like bran or oatbran are
ood for you, too — just add a few
trawberries, chopped banana or
each and a splash of skimmed milk
r a great, natural taste!

ATERWORKS

Forget fizzy drinks, tea or coffee
nd go for pure mineral water or
erbal tea instead.

Tea and coffee are loaded with
affeine which doesn't do you much
ood — so try fruit or herbal tea for a
hange.

Mineral water is great for
leansing your system, flushing
way all the impurities, leaving you
ith a glowing complexion. So, grab
ourself a bottle and try to drink
bout six glasses a day — try it with
'shot' of lemon or lime juice for
xtra taste!

HEALTHY HABITS!

Ask your mum to grill food like
sausages and bacon and see if you
can persuade her to try oven chips
to cut down on fat.

If you drink a glass of water before a
meal it'll take the edge off your
appetite and stop you eating too
much.

Go for yummy diet soft drinks
instead of sugar-filled ordinary
ones. If you like fresh fruit juice go
for a variety with no added sugar.

Take some scrummy wholemeal
sarnies for lunch instead of stodgy
school dinners. Try eating a low-fat
yoghurt with fruit instead of rice
pudding or apple crumble and
custard.

Make sure you have some fresh fruit
or juice for Vitamin C every day 'cos
your body can't store it. And don't
think vitamin tablets will make up for
a bad diet 'cos nothing beats the
real thing.

If you eat healthily you shouldn't
need to worry about counting
calories and the odd chocolate bar
or bag of crisps won't make any
difference!

CARBOHYDRATES — these are
foods like wholemeal bread, pasta,
rice and potatoes — they all give
you energy.

PROTEIN — this is found in some
green veggies (like broccoli),
chicken, fish etc. and is necessary
for healthy 'tissue' growth like skin,
hair, nails and inside your body too!

VITAMINS — essential for a healthy
body.

MINERALS — same as vitamins —
both are found in small amounts in
most fresh fruit and veg.

You should try to eat three
healthy meals every day which
should fill you up but there are times
when a small, tasty snack wouldn't
go amiss no matter what you've had
to eat!

But if you want to keep the
calories down go for these scrummy
snacks:

Fresh fruit
Sticks of fresh veggies like carrots,
celery or peppers
Crunchy muesli bars (without added
sugar)
Low-fat/diet yoghurts

Fill up on these and there won't
be any room for chocolate biccies!

Thanks to Yvonne and The Hawkhill Harriers.

Yvonne Reilly, an up an' comin' 1500 metres runner, tells us about life on the track!

GOLDEN *girl*

So, Yvonne, when did it all start?

"Well, I was in first year at school and I ran a local schools race. I won that, and that's when my coach, Margaret, noticed me. She asked me if I wanted to join the Hawkhill Harriers (local running team) and so I started training with them.

"I hadn't run before then at all — it just came to me!"

Do you do any other sports apart from this?

"No. I played hockey for the school, but since I got into running I gave it up in case I got injured. I played hockey on a Saturday, y'see, and I'd have a race on Sunday and I couldn't risk an injury, so I gave up hockey."

Is there anyone you admire in the running world?

"I like Yvonne Murray. She presented me with a medal at one race."

Yvonne meets Liz McColgan, a fellow Scottish runner.

A girl's gotta be fit!

What's been your fastest time for the 1500 metres?

"I ran 4 mins 38 seconds which is my personal best!" (P.S. This is *purritty* fast!)

and this season I want to train harder and get fitter. No, I never get bored! I've been doing it for three years and my enthusiasm never goes!"

Isn't your social life affected by all this running lark?

"Well, my friends play hockey so they understand, but on Saturday nights, I usually have to go in early 'cos I've usually got a race on Sunday. Friday nights are OK, but I train Tuesdays, Wednesdays and Thursdays and the rest of the time is taken up with schoolwork!"

So you're quite dedicated, then?

"Well, I'm getting more and more dedicated as I go on,

So it's a career move, this?

"I'd quite like to take up running as a career but if I'm not as good as I should be, I'd still do it as a hobby. If I keep going as I am just now, I'd like to run the way Liz McColgan does — professionally."

Some serious diet-watching's in order, then?

"Yeah, I *do* watch my diet. I eat lots of carbohydrates and loads of pasta. Occasionally I'll eat junk food — but not all the time!"

What do your teachers think of all this running business?

"I've never had any teacher complain, in fact my PE teachers are really keen on my running and they're always asking me how I'm getting on. I mean, they can't complain — I represented our school, Scottish Schools and now British Schools! I've always got time for my schoolwork."

Training in the chill o' the night!

Is it an expensive hobby?

"It's not that expensive, but for trainers, you've got to spend over £50 if you want something really good.

"I've got Nike Air trainers and you really notice the difference

between them and normal shoes. If you're starting off, you're better to get the cheaper ones."

Do you get nervous before races?

"In the leagues I don't usually get nervous, but before the British races, I was! I did cross country in Ireland and I was really nervous — it just seems to be in the International races!"

So has yer mom got a cabinet full o' trophies at home for you?

"Yeah, I've got about 40 trophies and 25 medals!"

What do you enjoy most about it?

"Doing competitions and seeing how much better you've become by beating people who've previously beaten *you,* or have been at the same level!"

And what don't you like, 'cos there must be something?!

"Em . . . there's nothing I hate about it — honestly!"

So what's the ultimate ambition for a runner like yerself? (Need we ask?!)

"I'd *love* to get to the Olympics! If I really trained hard and set my mind to it, maybe I could do it!"

WINTER

Chase the chill away with some silver and grey . . .

Wintry Tales

STONE TONES

Steely greys, silvers and stones are all big fashion news this season. You can 'team' them with cutesy pinks for a fluffy feline look, white for the preppy feel or with brights for a bolder impact.

MAKE-UP

Now that the cold winds are well 'n' truly blowin' make sure that your skin is v. well moisturised and that your lips are protected. Indeed, wearing make-up can actually protect your skin from the elements!

BASE — Use a creamy foundation applied to a recently moisturised skin. Sometimes with thicker foundations it's easier to use your fingers to apply it, going over the hairline, jawline, sides of mouth and around eyes with a slightly moist natural sponge. Use a ball of cotton wool and press your loose powder into your foundation — your base'll look smoother and last longer that way.

EYES — Use a white or v. light pink on the upper eyelid to emphasise your brow bones. Smudge steely grey eyeshadow over the middle of your eyelid, blending to either side with a soft brush — this'll make your eyes look rounder. A little bit of the same eyeshadow on the eyebrow will strengthen the effect. Use a little black mascara, combing the eyelashes in between each application.

LIPS — We kept it simple with just a slick o' cutesy pinky lippy. Apply it on top of your lip balm and it'll give you extra protection.

WINTER TIPS

● It's essential that you keep your lips well moisturised in the winter months as those blustery winds can wreak havoc. Take your foundation over your lips before applying a moisturising lipstick or if you don't wear make-up, be sure to wear a lip balm.

● If you suffer from cold sores, apply a dab of Blisteze or similar treatment the minute you can feel it. Meantime, lay off the kissing and don't share cups, lipsticks, towels or the like as you could spread the infection.

● It's oh-so-easy to eat a bad diet because of Christmas and the cold but it'll make slipping into these party dresses a v. depressing affair indeed. Eat plenty of tangerines, apples and fresh vegetables and try not to get too carried away with the selection boxes.

● If you're taking to the piste this winter, take an extra high S.P.F. with you. The reflecting sunbeams off the snow can burn you badly. Cover lips, nose, under your eyes and cheeks with a ski-block. A pair of sunglasses will protect your eyes from the glare too.

● Woolly tights are the order of the day or layer a couple o' pairs of cotton tights for a mega opaque effect!

● Ear muffs are cutesome and will save you from painfully cold ears!

◀◀ Jacket, scarf and gloves from Snob. ▶

JACKIE **87**

Pete was miles away in France — so it wouldn't matter if Michelle accepted Simon's invitation . . .

"MICHELLE, phone!" I charged downstairs to take the receiver from Mum.

Was it Pete again? Surely not. He'd already rung me twice this week. And all the way from France!

He was really missing me. Said he wished he hadn't gone. But I knew he'd had very little choice. A family holiday in France was what his Mum had wanted. And a family holiday in France was what she had got.

He's nice, Pete, a real sound guy. Quite good-looking too, if you like fair-haired types.

I'd been going out with him for most of the summer and we'd had a great time. Till his mum had dragged him off to France.

"Hi," I said, picking up the phone

My heart skipped a beat, when a deep husky voice replied.

"Hello there, remember me? Simon."

Wow, what a question, did I remember him? It was only that hunk I'd met at my cousin's party last week.

I'd gone because I was fed up. She's a bit older than me and I didn't know many of her friends. But seeing as most of my mates were on holiday, I needed to do something.

Sue was really nice and introduced me to loads of guys and girls. But the only person who really made an impression on me was Simon.

BUZZ

He was a real smoothie, different to any lad I had ever met before, with short black hair and big blue eyes. He was older too. And I got quite a buzz from the attention he paid to me.

"Hi, Simon." Somehow I managed to sound cool, and not squeak like I usually do when I'm excited.

There was a slight pause, as though Simon was waiting for me to say something else. Then he went on. "Look my mate's having a party tomorrow night. Would you like to come?"

Sorry but I can't, I was about to say. I'm already going out with someone.

Last week was all right 'cos we just danced and talked. But this would be a date. It would be different.

Then a wicked little voice in my head stopped me dead in my tracks.

"So what?" it whispered. "Go on, go to the party with him. He's a real dish. The kind of guy you've dreamed about for years. Forget Pete, he's not here. Anyway, he doesn't own you, does he?"

No, of course he doesn't. It was easy to agree with the voice. Easier still to say, "Yeah, that would be great!" to Simon.

"Right, I'll pick you up at your place about eight o'clock." Simon sounded neither pleased nor surprised.

Gulping I hung up, guilt overwhelming me. I wouldn't go. I'd ring Sue, get his number. Ask her why she had given him mine and my address. Then ring him and tell him that I already had a boyfriend, that we were an item and there was no room in my life for anyone else.

But what would I wear if I changed my mind?

That shirt and those leggings I'd seen in River Island last week.

I'd saved enough money from my Saturday job now to buy them. I could nip out of work in my lunch hour and dash to the store and get them.

I spent the rest of the evening doing my roots and pushing thoughts of Pete to the back of my mind, even though his face did keep thrusting itself to the front of it. He wouldn't know, none of our crowd would be there.

And what the eye doesn't see the heart doesn't grieve over, or so they say.

NOVELTY

Simon picked me up as arranged outside our house next night. It was quite a novelty getting into a car instead of waiting inside Boots' shop doorway for Pete to turn up.

I always seemed to arrive too early. He looked me over as we drove off and smugly I waited for a compliment, but all he said was, "It isn't fancy dress you know," as he stared at my new gear. "Why didn't you wear what you had on last week? That looked great."

He laughed as he spoke, taking the sting from his words, but I still felt awful.

I studied my fingernails intently wondering what to say. If it had been any other lad I'd have told him to get lost, then I'd have got out of the car and gone home.

The party was in full swing when we arrived and all the girls were dressed to kill in really elegant clothes. I felt really stupid.

OUT OF SIGHT ...

A deceitful short story by Veronica Robinson

Illustration by Carey Bennett.

Simon introduced me to everyone then left me in a corner with a glass in my hand, while he went to talk to his fan club.

Honestly, he knew more girls than I'd had hot dinners and they were all flocking round him as though he was a pop star.

Of course he was enjoying every minute of it, what boy wouldn't? They're all conceited, even the ugly ones. Except Pete. He's the most unconceited guy I know.

LONELY

Watching everyone laughing and talking together made me feel incredibly lonely. There was no one in the room I knew except Simon.

This wasn't really my scene, everyone here was older than me, more sophisticated. With my newly done hair and black and white clothes I looked like a golliwog. All I needed was a red shiny jacket.

My mind went back to Pete. Funny I never felt like this when I was with him. Pete made me feel good, he was always saying how much he liked my trendy gear.

Pangs of guilt came flooding over me. I wondered what he was doing so far away in France. Had he strayed like me? Was he out with some lovely French girl? I hoped not and deep down I knew that he wouldn't be. Pete wasn't like that.

Pete was a one girl guy. Unlike Simon, who would expect the girls in his life to share him. Suddenly I was glad there was no one here that I knew. No one who could tell Pete I had two timed him.

"Do you want to dance, Michelle?" At last Simon seemed to realise that he had brought me to the party. He spent the rest of the evening being really nice.

But it was no good. I'd gone off him. Was it really him I had fancied or just the image he portrayed of every girl's dream boy?

He took me home then parked the car and I realised with horror as he leaned forward that he was going to kiss me. At least he thought he was, and that was his biggest mistake. Opening the car door I did a runner, getting out so quickly that he banged his head on the window. And although I'm ashamed to admit it, I giggled. Well, he did look stupid.

Rubbing his head he gave me a dazed grin. "I'll see you sometime, Michelle," he muttered.

"Yeah," I replied, knowing as well as he did that I wouldn't.

Then I dashed into our house.

"Hi," Mum said. "Had a good time?" Then before I could answer, "Pete phoned to say he'll be glad when he's back."

"Me too," I replied, listening with a sense of relief to the sound of Simon's car engine starting up.

He'd be going back to the party no doubt and his fan club. Well they were welcome to him. I had Pete and he was all I wanted.

THE REAL THING?

Do you spend most of your time with your head in the clouds over your latest bloke, or have you got your Reeboks firmly on the ground? Answer these questions and find out . . .

1. When you think about him, what do you think about?
a) Living happily every after . . . with him!
c) His pathetic taste in music, his smelly feet, the annoying way he never phones when he says . . . and his cute best friend!
b) The good laughs you've had together and when you're going to see him next.

2. OK, so we all know he's not Mr Junior Gaultier of the year, but this time he turns up at the local disco in a not-so-fetching pair of Timmy Mallet style Bermuda shorts and a pink baseball cap — in the middle of winter! What's your reaction?
c) What is this — his idea of a joke? He can bloomin' well go home and change right now if he expects you to even look at him! This is just not funny and he's heading for the big 'E' if he doesn't smarten up!
a) He could turn up in a pair of brown cords and a yellow tank top for all you care. He's still the same person underneath, and it doesn't matter a jot how ridiculous he looks!
b) You'd laugh at his knobbly knees, but just hope he doesn't do it again!

3) How would you describe your boyfriend?
c) He's a handsome devil with wads of cash, he's crazy about you, so he'll do for the time being!
a) Perfection on legs! There's no way you'd go out with anyone else, he's the one for you!
b) Basically, he's a good laugh. You enjoy his company and you trust him, you know his faults and like him just the same!

4) Is there anything that niggles you about him?
a) Not really, but you get quite huffy when he goes out with the lads, without you. It's not that you don't trust him, you just want to be with him.
c) You can't stand the way he has to 'burp' after drinking a can of Fanta and the way he goes on about Winona Ryder and why does he always have to tap his left foot and pretend to play the drums all the time?
b) Maybe a few small things, but then you like his little imperfections too!

5. You're at a New Year party, with your 'other half' when, all of a sudden, you spy the most gorgeous creature ever to walk the earth! What's more he's heading your way . . . what do you do?
c) Well, you'd do what any self-respecting party girl would do — plank a smacker on his lips yelling 'Happy New Year!', then slip away to a quiet corner, out of your boyfriend's sight . . .
a) The only gorgeous creature you've got eyes for is your very own boyfriend. You don't look twice at anyone else!
b) A quick 'New Year' peck on the cheek is all he gets, then you set about finding your boyfriend to tell him how much in demand you are! Just to keep him on his toes, of course!

6. Oh dear! It's 8 p.m. and he was supposed to phone an hour ago. What do you do?
a) You sit by the phone, wondering what on earth you've done to deserve such a punishment. Eventually you pluck up the courage to call him, only to discover his sister had been using the phone non-stop all night. Phew! What a relief!
c) Well, he's blown it, hasn't he? You go round to your best mate's and head out for a night on the town . . . as a single gal again!
b) You presume he's forgotten, silly blighter, and give him a call the following night, with a sharp ticking off. You're not that bothered though, he's only human.

7. It's Saturday night and you're just adding the finishing touches to your lippy 'cos you're going to a mega party with your best mate, when your boyfriend phones, loaded with the cold, and looking for a bit of sympathy. He wants you to go and visit him. What do you do?
b) Pop round with a box of choccies, listen to his complaining for an hour, then go to the party!
c) Tell him to take a Lemsip and quit moaning! It's not your problem, so you hang up on him and make for the party.
a) The poor soul! One sniff from him is all it takes and you're by his side with a 'get well soon' card, mopping his brow for the rest of the evening. Who cares about the party, you wouldn't have enjoyed it anyway!

8. What's your idea of a fun time?
b) You, your boyfriend and all of your mates at a disco, dancing the night away 'til 2 a.m.
a) Snuggled up with your bloke, a soppy movie and a ham 'n' mushroom pizza.
c) A loud karaoke with your friends, no boyfriends allowed!

9. Have you ever told your boyfriend you love him?
c) Never. No way, you're not that serious and you never will be.
a) Millions of times. You tell him every day at least 10 times!
b) Only a couple of times, and he knows you mean it.

10. What's the best thing about going out with him?
a) It makes your life worth living.
c) Just being able to say you've got a boyfriend, really.
b) The good times you have together.

Mostly a's . . .
Bring out the violins, girl, you've got it bad! We're surprised you even managed to do this quiz, without floating off to Planet Lurve! You'd better loosen up and try not to take relationships so seriously, you don't want to end up disappointed! This ain't love, it's infatuation!

Mostly b's . . .
Good for you! You like a bit of romance but you're sensible enough not make a soppy fool of yourself! You're obviously close to your boyfriend, but you still don't let him rule your life. You still go out with your friends as much as you did, keep it up!

Mostly c's . . .
Love . . . what's that? You hate the idea of romance and reach for the sick bag at the thought of being a 'couple'! The idea of a relationship scares you beyond belief! It's all very well to enjoy your freedom, as long as you don't hurt your boyfriend's feelings. He won't put up with it for long, y'know!

CHART
Check out our chart

BOYS ▶ GIRLS ▼	ARIES	TAURUS
ARIES	You'll have some great times at first but it won't last.	A bit stormy with lots of arguments.
TAURUS	Exciting and passionate but could burn itself out.	You're too stubborn and neither of you will back down in an argument.
GEMINI	Lots in common. You'll always have plenty to do.	Solid and stable but not very exciting.
CANCER	An unlikely match but don't let anyone talk you out of it!	This could be the best thing that's happened to you!
LEO	You're optimistic about the way things are going.	You find each other irresistible!
VIRGO	Watch out for those tempers. They're both a bit short!	You can depend on this one and it'll be great fun, too.
LIBRA	You're a bit of a challenge for each other.	You're quite happy to let the other get on with their own thing.
SCORPIO	Why can't you have little problems like everyone else?	You really fancy each other but there's not much else to keep you together.
SAGITTARIUS	You both love to do things spontaneously.	You'll be wondering what you ever saw in each other.
CAPRICORN	A bit boring if you don't make the effort.	Very strong. You won't let the other one down.
AQUARIUS	You'll get on pretty well together.	Don't let past loves get in the way.
PISCES	A bit too temperamental to be much good together.	You like things to be peaceful and relaxed.

SUCCESS!
to find your perfect partner . . .

GEMINI	CANCER	LEO	VIRGO
Plenty of fun and excitement from beginning to end!	You don't find it very easy to talk to each other.	Very passionate. Lucky you!	You're both very emotional. Be careful about arguments.
Could be boring if you don't put in some effort.	You two were made for each other!	You both think the other's pretty gorgeous, but that's about it.	Long-lasting and happy. Make the most of it.
You find it quite difficult to talk over problems.	Take things slowly. There's no point in jumping in head first.	You don't take each other for granted. A very rewarding relationship.	Don't get too involved. You're not really a good match.
A bit boring but you can liven things up pretty easily!	You're both so dreamy, you'll have a wonderful time.	Looks like you've got the balance right.	You'll stick together through thick and thin.
You don't always see eye to eye. It could cause a few sulks.	A bit troublesome but it shouldn't cause too many problems.	Far too competitive with each other.	Is it worth it when you have to work so hard to keep it together?
You could be together for ages.	You'll get on very well together.	Your personalities make this a strong relationship.	There'll be a lot of ups and downs. It's your funny moods, you know!
What is it about each other you find so fascinating?	A lot of difficulties could make it unhappy.	If you're looking for excitement, this is where to find it!	Constant criticism is enough to ruin any relationship.
You give the impression you couldn't care less.	You won't want to break up once you've got together.	You don't have much in common but sometimes it doesn't matter.	You were just waiting for your ideal romance, weren't you?
Too argumentative to get on really well.	You're not very positive about this, are you?	Great if you're looking for excitement.	You're not very committed to each other.
You enjoy each other's company no matter what you're doing.	If one has a problem, the other will be very supportive.	You're not prepared to settle for second best!	You know you could have a brilliant time together.
You're completely different but it shouldn't matter too much.	You fall out over the slightest thing.	Very deep and meaningful. A bit too deep perhaps?	There's not a lot of excitement going on here.
Your friends think you're far too soppy with each other.	You're a bit starry-eyed but you have reason to be!	Sparks fly when you get together. A pity, really. You could be great together.	You're bound to have some great times!

CHART SU

LIBRA	SCORPIO	SAGITTARIUS	CAPRICORN
They say opposites attract. But you'll have to put in some effort to make it work.	The combination of emotions make it a very balanced relationship.	Both of you are very romantic. Look forward to candlelit dinners and lots of pressies.	Can be rocky, but you'll get over the difficult patches.
You both love romance in the first stages.	A bit over-powering. Can become claustrophobic.	You'll be able to overcome any difference of opinion.	Safe and dependable. Some would say even a bit boring.
Once you two get together, there's no stopping you.	A little mystery can be very exciting!	There'll be a few problems but can you sort them out?	At first it could be difficult. You're both too stubborn!
You're very thoughtful and care a lot about each other.	Very intense. Are you up to it?	You don't have much in common and it's not really worth pursuing.	Very similar people. Not always a good thing!
You love to be affectionate with each other.	It'll be exciting at first but it might fizzle out.	You share the same sense of humour. Always a winner!	There are only so many arguments you can take.
You won't nag each other all the time.	You'll be lucky if you ever agree on anything!	So laid-back you'll wonder why every one else has so many problems!	You'll never be able to decide about who pays.
Don't get too serious, it may not be a permanent thing.	You'll find each other pretty intriguing.	An unusual match but you should have a great time together.	You know what makes the other one tick.
Briefer than you'd hoped but you made the best of it!	You're drawn to each other no matter what.	A little tense sometimes but usually interesting.	A bit over-emotional but very loving.
You sloppy things — how romantic can you get!	You don't like to cause any trouble for each other.	Nothing spectacular but it works well.	You'd be better off with someone else.
If you like each other that much then just go for it!	You can't do better than this.	You don't have much in common to keep you together.	A great match. Don't mess it up.
What a great couple you'll make.	Interest at first will soon wear off. Sorry!	You'll have a great laugh together and that's really important.	Nobody will dare to come between you.
A few ups and downs but nothing you can't handle.	You're not sure how serious you're prepared to get.	There are too many hassles to make it worth your while.	You'll want to rush things and it's not the best way to go about it.

CCESS!

AQUARIUS	PISCES	BOYS ◀ GIRLS ▼
Fine, but don't expect anything long-lasting.	Keeping secrets from each other isn't going to help.	**ARIES**
Needs a lot of work. But are you prepared to make the effort?	Nothing very serious but lots of fun!	**TAURUS**
Very like-minded. A good balance.	Lack of trust will get you nowhere.	**GEMINI**
A fatal attraction. Maybe there's someone else involved?	You really love each other. Aaah!	**CANCER**
You think the other won't understand your feelings and you're probably right.	A great match — you'll be very good for each other.	**LEO**
Pretty insensitive when it comes to feelings.	You love a bit of romance to liven things up.	**VIRGO**
Jealousy could be one of your major problems.	You're very different people but it might just work.	**LIBRA**
You love yourselves too much to be able to love each other!	You'll get along just fine.	**SCORPIO**
You both love adventure.	You're very attracted to each other in every way.	**SAGITTARIUS**
It's not a competition. Be content with what you've got.	You're very secure. Trust is everything to you.	**CAPRICORN**
One's a lot more keen than the other.	You prefer not to be tied to one person.	**AQUARIUS**
You argue at every opportunity. Can you really be bothered?	Lucky you! Looks like you've found what you've been looking for.	**PISCES**

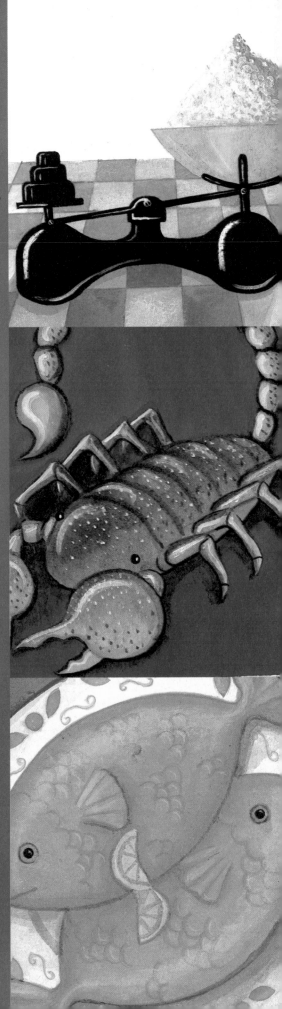

10 REASONS SHOULD

1. First for fashion — what to wear and where to find it!
2. Pin-ups a-plenty of your fave pop, film and TV stars!
3. The best photo stories around.
4. Boys — and all you've ever wanted to know about 'em!
5. Beauty made easy! Just follow our tips for make-up, hair and skin care.

Dear Mr/Mrs Newsagent,
    Please reserve/deliver a copy of **JACKIE MAGAZINE** for me each and every week.

Name ....

Address ....
....
....